A DISTRICT NURSE IN RURAL WALES BEFORE THE NATIONAL HEALTH SERVICE

Best wishes

David Mills-Owens

(Leon)

Frontispice: *Nurse Mills Evans (in carpet slippers!), with fellow members of the Llanfair Caereinion Women's Institute, visiting Trafalgar Square, London, on Thursday, June 10 1948.*

'Several hundred members of the Montgomeryshire Federation of Women's Institutes took part in an outing to London, organised by Mrs Sockett, the county secretary, on Thursday. The train left Welshpool at 6.30 a.m. and the return journey was begun at 11.30 p.m. from Paddington.'
– The Montgomeryshire Express, Saturday June 12 1948, p.6, col.3, under Llanfair Caereinion news.

Front row: left to right: Mrs Maud Pryce, Tanllan (later Brynawelon); Nurse Mills Evans; Miss M. Watkin, Emporium; Olwen Jones, Llwyfarch; Mrs Hilda Hewitt (formerly Honorary Secretary, Llanfair C. Nursing Association); Miss Phylis Astley, Corner Shop; Mrs Hill, High Street; Mrs Maedndy Jones, Preswylfa (Chemist's Shop); Mrs Mary Morgan, Preston House; Mrs Bennet, High Street; ?Mrs Jones, Tanyffridd.

Rear: left to right: Mrs Thomas, Eithnog Farm; Mrs I. Annwyl Evans, Liverpool House; Miss Watkin, Emporium; Mrs Theodora Hamer Jones, Tynyfawnog; unidentified member; ?Mrs Davies, Penheber; ?Miss Jones, Tanyffridd; Mrs Jones, Tynyfawnog.

A District Nurse in rural Wales before the National Health Service

David Mills Evans
(also known as 'Leon Evans')

Edited and prepared for publication
by Dr W.T.R. Pryce

First edition: 2003

© Text: David Mills Evans

ISBN: 0-86381-851-X

Cover design: Sian Parri

First published in 2003 by
Gwasg Carreg Gwalch, 12 Iard yr Orsaf, Llanrwst, Wales LL26 0EH
℡ 01492 642031   🖷 01492 641502
🖳 books@carreg-gwalch.co.uk   Internet: www.carreg-gwalch.co.uk

Cover photo:
Nurse, with baby Ann Griffiths,
Garthllwyd Farm, Llanfair C.,
born November 1940
(original: Mrs Ann Closman, Haverfordwest)

For my two daughters, Ann and Sara,
who, in later years may appreciate their Nain.
Hopefully, they will inherit some of her qualities;
and for my granddaughter, Caoimhe Harley,
born January 22 2001.

'I must go. It is my duty'

– Nurse Mills Evans, MBE, 1899-1964

Born at Brongeifr, Y Fan, Llanidloes, 1899
Died Llanfair Caereinion, 1964

District Nurse and Midwife, Llanfair Caereinion 1920-1964

Contents

Foreword

Nurse Mills Evans is a legend of Llanfair Caereinion. Indeed, she was a legend in her lifetime. I had the undoubted honour of working with her for a short time towards the end of her career. My father, Doctor Walter Milton Jones, General Practioner of Medicine at Llanfair 1919-67, started his career one year before the arrival of Nurse in 1920. He knew her well and admired her work. Without doubt, he, too, could have written a book on her many contributions. I wish I had. But there was no time for such things.

As the reader will soon discover, Nurse served in an area that was and continues to be deeply rural. She travelled the district on foot, horseback, bicycle and by any other means available. I recall many occasions when I would be sitting in comfort on a tractor – in truth, occasionally, perhaps I was hanging on for dear life! – when I would meet the Nurse tramping in the snow, always carrying her black bag, to join me to attend a patient.

It is good to have this life recorded, to bring to mind the difficulties and hardships of those times – a far cry from today's medicine. It cannot be easy for the present generation to imagine just how things were.

I have fond memories of a truly warm-hearted, hard working and dedicated lady.

Dr John Milton Jones
Brynglas Hall, Llanfair Caereinion,
General Practitioner of Medicine at
Llanfair Caereinion 1952-1982.

Editor's Foreword

In many respects, this is a remarkable book. It is remarkable in its origins. It is remarkable for the account that it gives. It is remarkable for the written record that it provides. *A District Nurse in Rural Wales before the National Health Service* is the original work of David Mills Evans. Even today, he is still widely known as 'Leon Evans', a nickname given him in childhood in admiration of his robust personality. Throughout his life, Mr Evans has followed the craft of painter and decorator, working for many years with his father and brother. His family firm has undertaken painting and redecorating jobs in houses, offices and shops, schools and for many public buildings throughout Montgomeryshire – indeed, even further afield. His family are well known and widely respected in his own community of Llanfair Caereinion. Mr Evans left school at the age of 15 and joined the war-time Royal Navy. Every school holiday was spent helping his father in his work; and later, every spell of leave from the Navy was spent back home in Montgomeryshire working in the family business. Yet, without any formal academic studies in the techniques of research methods, Mr Evans has given us a marvellous cameo, recording the friendly way of life in a small town and the surrounding rural communities in the 1930s, immediately before and during the years of World War II, and in the years that followed.

That achievement would have been fully acceptable on its own. But the mother of Mr David Mills Evans is the person who dominates this story. For some forty-five years, she was the District Nurse serving the town of Llanfair Caereinion and its extensive rural upland hinterland. Nurse Mills Evans brought into this world men and women who still live in the communities of the Banw valley as well as countless others who have moved away – including members of my own family. This fascinating book chronicles her many years of devoted service –

especially the difficulties that the district nurse had to face in serving remote rural communities before the establishment of our National Health Service. So, in a very real way this book is also a historical record of much achievement under challenging conditions.

But, in bringing all these themes together, Mr David Mills Evans clearly reveals how closely 'Nurse', as everyone referred to his mother, was involved in her own community. She worked closely with local doctors, the clergy and social workers, but she also ran the family shop and the family contracting business for the full range of painting and decorating services. Selling sweets, paint brushes or panes of glass in the family shop, delivering a baby in a remote hillside farm, coping with wartime food restrictions, bringing up her own two sons, laying out the dead, preparing quotations for the family firm to undertake the redecoration of a cluster of primary schools in Montgomeryshire – all came within the scope of her everyday duties. Nurse was a deeply committed Christian woman and an active member of her chapel. Her kindness included caring for the personal welfare of other people; especially young women who sought to enter the nursing profession. In this account of her life and work, the regular duties of the district nurse are intertwined with the family business of plumbing, painting and decorating and with public duties and obligations – all typical of life in a closely integrated society such as was the town of Llanfair Caereinion in the 1930s and 1940s.

Fortunately, due to the vigilance and foresight of Mrs Megan Roberts, the rules of the Llanfair Caereinion and District Nursing Association have been saved from destruction. At one stage some of these reports had been sent for disposal as waste paper! A selection of these, which constitute an important record of the families and individuals who supported the local nursing association, is reproduced in the Appendices. Since these contain invaluable information not available in any other source, they constitute important primary sources that will be of considerable interest to researchers concerned with the origins of the National Health Service as well as family and community historians.

It has been my pleasure to undertake the editorial work on behalf of Mr David Mills Evans and to prepare his original text for publication. Here and there in the text there are mentions of costs and charges. The prices cited have changed considerably since the late 1930s and 1940s. For that reason we have inserted present-day valuations in the text (but not in the Appendices). These have been derived using the computer program *Value of the Pound, 1600-1999* (Drake Software Associates, 2001).

Oral history has provided much of the prime source material for this book. Whilst the informant is alert, mental images can be recalled but, unlike documentary records, which survive long after the individual person, inevitably memories are of limited duration unless written down or recorded by other means. The full achievement of this important book is that it constitutes a fascinating record of community life as well as an informed account of the work of the district nurse in upland countryside and within a small market town some two generations ago, in the mid-twentieth century, before the establishment of the National Health Service. It is significant that much of the content has been verified by long-resident members of the local community. Apart from the printed 'rules' of the local nursing association and the lists of subscribers, no other extant documentary sources cover these themes. In a very real sense, therefore, the contents of this book could never have been written without the resource of memory. And so, this written account is, in itself, original and of considerable value as a community record.

Dr W. T. R. Pryce,
Visiting Reader in the Cultural and Historical Geography of Wales, Faculty of Social Sciences, The Open University in Wales, Cardiff. December 2002.

Figures

Preface

At the outset it was my intention to write an account of my mother, Nurse Hannah Mills Evans, and her life work. But, because she became heavily involved with our family retail business and the contract work of painting and decorating, anecdotes from that side of our family life crept into the story as well as memories of some old local characters, customs and life in a small town, especially during the war years between 1939 and 1945.

Why I wrote this account I really do not know. Maybe it is an attempt to record events that are soon forgotten – events never to be seen again. My wife, Mary, also a dedicated nurse, has encouraged me to make this effort – even though, sometimes, I never felt capable of completing the task. I am much indebted to the following friends who have loaned some of the old and now rare photographs reproduced in this book: Ella Groves of Woodbridge, Suffolk, daughter of Nurse Pricilla Gethin (Fig. 4); David Morgan, Melinyddol, Llanfair (Fig. 10); Andy Ridell, Stockport (Fig. 11); Ivor Brown, Croeso, Llanfair (Fig. 14); Stanley Jones, Paris House, Llanfair (Fig. 15); Primrose Evans, Watergate Street, Llanfair (Fig. 16); and Marian Morgan, Mount Einion, Llanfair (Figs. 12, 18-20). I am grateful to Councillor Ken Astley, Gwernybrain, and Ceinwen Williams, Pantymilwyr, for additional information on the fighter plane crash at Rhiwhiriaeth recorded in Chapter 3 and, also, Jeff Hill, Welshpool, for Fig. 3. Dr Pryce took the photographs included as Figures 13 and 17 especially for this book. I am much indebted to Megan Roberts, Tegla, for saving some of the printed records of the Llanfair Caereinion and District Nursing Association, which had been sent to be burnt. These lists of subscribers are valuable as sources because these include the names of many local people who supported the work of my mother. Due to the foresight of Mrs Roberts, we now make these widely available by reprinting them as appendices to this book.

I wish to acknowledge the kind help of Dr John Milton Jones, Brynglas, Llanfair for encouraging me to prepare this work, especially his Foreword in tribute to the life and work of my late mother. Many others have assisted me, especially Mrs Elsie Astley, Tŷ Newydd, Llangynyw, who was the first to consider my work worth publishing; Mrs Ursula Astley, Hafandeg, Llanfair; Trefor Issac, Maesglas, Llanfair; Huw Davies, Minyddol, Llanerfyl; Mrs Margaret Stacey of the Montgomeryshire Library at Newtown, and Mr John Ellis, formerly Deputy Head at Ysgol Uwchradd Caereinion. I am grateful to the specialist staff at the National Library of Wales for their expertise in tracing some of the more rare published works to which reference is made in the text. My brother, John Mills Evans, Bro Enddwyn, Dyffryn Ardudwy, Gwynedd, helped in the recall of some of the experiences recorded in this book and he provided the original for Figure 7 and other material.

My original text has been expertly edited and prepared for publication by Dr W. T. R. Pryce of the Faculty of Social Sciences at the Open University, who, also, is a native of Llanfair Caereinion. I am grateful to him for his committed interest and support. Mrs Mary Steele produced the first draft of my original text in word-processed form. Mr Simon Bright, formerly Development Office for the Llanfair Caereinion and District Forum, set up under the Market Towns Initiative Scheme, facilitated my work in the early stages. I thank the Executive Committee of the Forum as well as The Open University in Wales for assistance towards some of the costs involved in preparing my original text for publication. Miss P. M. Davies of Llanidloes, Honorary Secretary of the Powysland Club, read through the final text. The editor and I are grateful for all her comments and suggestions. I am indebted to Mr Myrddin ap Dafydd and his colleagues at Gwasg Carreg Gwalch in Llanrwst for their high-quality work as publishers, so making this account of my mother, and her work, available to a wide readership.

David Mills Evans
Glanafon
Llanfair Caereinion

December 2002

CHAPTER ONE

The Early Years

When I was home bound recovering from an operation in hospital I had the time to read, something I enjoy doing very much. Until my enforced inactivity, time for reading was very limited and the daily press was sufficient. During this period of inactivity I read two books by Alf Strange. In *Me Dad's the Village Blacksmith* (1983) Strange has written about life in the Shropshire village of Welsh Frankton where his life had centered around his father's smithy. His second book, *Following Me Dad* (Strange 1986) relates more to general life in a Shropshire village and recalled events that had occurred in a small rural community. Strange's grandfather had come to work as a smith in Welsh Frankton in the late 1800s. Born in 1925, Alf Strange himself had followed his father into his trade.

These are wonderful recollections. For future generations they provide good insights into the work of the village blacksmith, now mostly defunct, and also into the life in a small Shropshire village. The fact that a blacksmith could have so many stories and events to relate came across to me very strongly. I, too, am from a small town community, once a village – a person with a story to tell of a way of life that will never be seen again. My mother was the district nurse and midwife between 1921 and 1964, serving rural communities around the small town of Llanfair Caereinion in rural central Wales for some forty-three years.

Originally, I intended to write an account about my mother, her nursing duties and the many incidents that I can recall. But my father ran a business in which mother became closely involved, eventually running it herself. Consequently, many of the incidents recorded in this book concern that side of our family life. Some of my recorded memories relate more to the community in which we have lived rather than to the nursing profession or our family business as painters and decorators; and provide glimpses of community life in Llanfair Caereinion, especially during the war years 1939-45.

My mother joined the Montgomeryshire Nursing Association on September 18th, 1919. The whole of her career was spent in serving Llanfair Caereinion town and the surrounding districts. The area in which she served was one of the largest, with some of the most deeply rural and remotest communities in Wales. It stretched from Dolmaen in the west and almost to Welshpool in the east, and from the upland Cefncoch community almost to Carno. Her area included the extensive Llanfihangel-yng-Nghwynfa district almost to Llanwddyn. Mam's nursing duties took her along some 1,300 miles of country roads and rough farm tracks. Regularly, each month she covered 1,200 miles in carrying out her responsibilities.

Mam, one of a large family, was born at Y Fan, near Llanidloes. Her father was a farmer and timber feller, using shire horses for these operations. She was educated at Manledd, a small country school north of Llanidloes, long since closed. All her sisters were educated there also: two became, like mother, State Registered Nurses and State Certified Midwives, in Llanidloes and in Manchester respectively; another went on to become a teacher after attending Llanidloes County School and Y Coleg Normal in Bangor.

The standards of teaching at Manledd school must have been high; for in the list of personal subscriptions to the local Nursing Association 1917-18 for the Rhiwhiriaeth district of Llanfair

Caereinion was included the name of a Mrs Hamer, School House (see Appendix B). Her husband had been the local headmaster and, like mother, he, also, had been educated at Manledd school. Mother's family name was that of 'Mills'. This distinctive name has been kept on in successive generations because of our family's pride in the fact that in the past some of them were well known as 'Y Millsiaid o Lanidloes', famous as Welsh hymn writers (see Ifor ap Gwilym, 1978, 103-11).

Mother was born in 1899 and left school at the age of fourteen. Initially she went into domestic service as a maid, the only occupation available for young girls in those days but by 1916 she had started her general nursing training at Plaistow, near Barking, in Essex. The training course lasted three years and, as mentioned earlier, Mam joined the Montgomeryshire Nursing Association in 1919. The probable reason why she did not take up her duties in the Llanfair district immediately is the fact that after her general training she had to complete midwifery training (Figure 1). When mother eventually moved to Llanfair in 1920 she met up with a Mrs Edwards of Neuadd Farm: they had both qualified as nurses together at Plaistow. It seems that many young women from Montgomeryshire qualified as nurses at that particular hospital. Soon, mother was known to everyone as 'the Nurse' or, as she preferred, just as 'Nurse'.

The National Health Service did not come into existence until 1947. Up to that date the Llanfair District Nursing Association was affiliated to the Montgomeryshire Nursing Association which was administered from the County Health Offices in Newtown under the County Medical Officer of Health (Appendix A). Dr Owen Morris was the County Medical Officer for Health at the start of mother's nursing career (Figure 2). He was followed by a Dr Felix Richards, the elder, and then by his son, also known as Dr Felix Richards. Mother's career spanned the periods of office of all these men.

Transport, especially to remote farmsteads was always a

problem, especially in the winter months. In the early years walking, cycling or riding on horseback was the only means by which mother could discharge her duties. Eventually, however, motorcycles and later small motor cars became important means of transport for the rural district nurse. Before her marriage, when Mam had only a bicycle for transport, the Nurse received a callout to a farm about half a mile from Llanfair town, situated some way off the main road. So, Mam left her bicycle by the side of the main road and walked up to the farm. On her return the bicycle had gone and mother walked home. Eventually it was returned by local youths with profound apologies: one of the youths, who was later to become her brother-in-law, had hidden the bicycle behind the hedgerow as a practical joke.

Despite many demands on her time, life for Nurse was not all work and no play. Mother enjoyed playing goalkeeper for the Llanfair Ladies Hockey team on a pitch on a fairly level field behind the local Observation post (Royal Observer Corps, see Pryce 1991, 27, 172) on Cae Boncyn but the climb up to the pitch was itself a tiring exercise. These must have been friendly matches as no reports of any the matches they played can be found in local newspapers. Our family were the proud owners of a wireless set (radio) something very few households owned and it was not until the early 1950s that TV sets arrived in Llanfair. Our wireless set was run by direct current electricity supplied by the Llanfair Electric Light Society from the mill at Melinyddol. Not all households were wired for electricity and the public supply was confined to the town only. Later, those homes without electricity used wireless sets run on wet batteries which had to be recharged regularly for a small fee. The man in charge and responsible for all electrical problems in the town was known to everyone as 'Evans Electric Light' (see Pryce, 1991, 58-59, 160-61).

If some big event was being broadcast on the wireless, a crowd would gather outside the open window of our house on the main street (Bridge Street) to listen in. I can recall a world heavyweight boxing championship contest between the Welshman Tommy Farr and the 'Brown Bomber', Joe Louis. The fight took place in America in August 1937. Consequently, we received the broadcast in the early hours of the morning. Even so, there was quite a large gathering outside our house. It was some time later that my father took my brother and I to see the film of the fight at the Clive Cinema in Welshpool (the large building, formerly a fannel factory, situated behind the Spar supermarket off Church Street in the town). The supporting film was a real tear jerker called 'Tugboat Annie'!

The collection of the payments for the local nursing service was the responsibility of the Nurse herself and this was the arrangement that continued until the advent of the National Health Service. The monies collected by Nurse were then handed over to the Secretary of the Llanfair Nursing Association. For many years this latter office was held by the late Mrs Hewitt, wife of the headmaster of the old Church School (Mr Hewitt later transferred to the teaching staff of the Llanfair High School, now Ysgol Uwchradd Caereinion). Either my brother or myself were given the job of taking these payments to Mrs Hewitt. Nurse was very meticulous about money matters, as became fully evident in later years when she also ran the family painting and decorating business.

On numerous occasions when people could not afford to pay for her services, Nurse waived the fee. In 1969 I met a gentleman who sang the praises of my mother. He told me he couldn't afford the confinement fee for the birth of his daughter, then in her twenties. He was never asked to pay for the Nurse's services. I am not sure how the costs were eventually covered. Nurse may have been careful with money, yet, in time of need, she could be very generous. The family of a local lady once told me about their mother who lived in a Llanfair street opposite a milliner's shop. Their mother was dying, and every time Nurse went to visit her it became plain that the elderly declining lady had taken a fancy to one of the hats on display in the milliner's shop window. So my mother bought it for her.

Some gypsies or travelling people used to camp occasionally on various sites around Llanfair. If one of the gypsy women was expecting a baby, usually Nurse was not contacted until the last minute. The birth of a child appears to be the only reason for such travelling people to stop on the same site for any length of time – just long enough for the new child to be registered. On one such occasion mother was summoned to a confinement late at night: the baby duly arrived shortly after midnight. It was the duty of the Nurse to visit mothers and their newborn every day for the ten days that followed. On the final visit, Nurse went to pay her customary visit, hoping to collect the standard fee of seventeen shillings and six pence (87$\frac{1}{2}$p, but the equivalent, today, of about £43). However, often the travellers would have gone, never to be heard of again, to continue their travels, whilst the bill from Llanfair Nursing Association was left unpaid.

Nurse experienced further problems with travelling people during the war years (1939-45). These particular gypsies had camped on some waste ground at Llwydiarth, close to Lake Vyrnwy (Llyn Efyrnwy), constructed to provide the main supply of public water to Liverpool. Being wartime, strict air-raid precautions were in force, one of them being that no lights could be shown; and for this reason all windows were covered with 'black-out' curtains. Because Lake Vyrnwy was near, potentially a prime target for German bombers, special care had to be taken. Rather late in this particular sequence of events and, as often happened, during the hours of darkness, Nurse was called out to yet another midwifery case. One of the necessities in childbirth is the need for an ample supply of hot water; but the only means the gypsies had of providing this was from a pot hanging over an open fire on a tripod. The fire was blazing away merrily when an Air Raid Warden approached, demanding that the offending fire be put out immediately. After a great deal of persuasion by Nurse, she won the day: the fire was allowed to stay and the baby was delivered safe and well. To mother this achievement was much more important than any German bomb.

After having been appointed to the Llanfair District, the first baby that Nurse delivered was born on the 16th of May, 1920. He turned out to be the well-known character, Wyn Penlan. Sadly, he passed away in 1994. On numerous occasions before the war mother was asked to judge baby beauty contests at local shows, but some mothers, whose babies had not been awarded anything, could become very upset. This, in turn, upset Nurse. In consequence, she always hated being asked to judge these events. To our Mam, all babies were beautiful. Thankfully, baby shows are now a thing of the past.

Throughout my father's working life, mother continued with her nursing duties. During her nursing career she never once took a formal holiday. However, on most Boxing Days, weather permitting, we would drive over to Llanidloes and Y Fan to see her parents and sisters at Manledd Farm. Not only did she carry out all her nursing duties but Nurse also ran our family shop selling household paints and wallpapers. To enable her to carry out her work a maid was employed to help out with domestic duties.

CHAPTER TWO

The District Nursing Association

For a number of years Y Foel, Llangadfan and Llanerfyl had a district nurse of their own but around the outbreak of the war in 1939 the whole of the Upper Banw district became part of mother's responsibilities. This increased the vast area for which she was now responsible to some 140 square miles. Despite added responsibilities, her salary remained the same. Although the Llanfair Caereinion District Nursing Association was established in 1912, the printed Annual Report for 1917-18, and the Association's 'Rules and Fees', c.1923, seem to be the earliest records that have survived (see Appendices). Recently, the Minute Book of the Association, covering the period from April 1932 to June 1948, has been found.

A committee of extremely able local people ran the Association. They ensured that the bills for Nurse's duties were paid, that any available grants were applied for, and they organised the house-to-house collections throughout Llanfair town and the surrounding countryside. Their commitment ensured that a district nurse/midwife was available at all times. The Upper Banw Nursing Association had had, intermittently, their own nurse, but in April 1932 they needed to draw on services from Nurse Evans. However, the payments for this work were not completed until January 1933. It was at this time, also, that the County Health Committee wanted Nurse Mills

Evans to take a refresher course at Plaistow Hospital in Essex but the Llanfair Association decided that this was not convenient. So, the County Committee sent the Upper Banw Nurse on the course whilst my mother covered her duties. From the records it seems that the Upper Banw Nursing Association was without a nurse from 1938 onwards. Consequently, my mother had to carry out all the necessary duties for these communities; and there were many ongoing administrative arguments between members of the Llanfair and Upper Banw Nursing Associations, especially over payments.

One of the biggest problems, which gave rise to much controversy, was the failure of the County Health Committee to define boundaries precisely between the areas served by different associations. This first problem arose in May 1934 when it was not known which district nurse was responsible for a family then living at Maespryd Farm, in the parish of Manafon. Eventually, responsibility was accepted by the neighbouring Tregynon Nursing Association. Exactly twelve months later, a similar boundary question arose again and the decision as to which nursing association was responsible was not finally settled until guidance had been obtained from Mr Thomas Oliver Roberts, of Llanfair Caereinion, a local school teacher and historian.

The Minute Book records that, during the later 1930s, the Upper Banw Nursing Association was drawing on the services of Nurse Mills Evans so frequently that the Llanfair Association decided that they would have to send a conveyance for her use. The Minutes frequently include comments on transport arrangements – a significant consideration in any wide-spread rural community. In 1932, for example, they recorded that 'the bicycle supplied to Nurse Evans from Mr Llewellyn Jehu gives satisfaction'. After several motorcycles, which Mam had used since 1923, a small car was purchased in 1935; and in June 1936 the County Nursing Association granted Nurse £10 per annum for its upkeep.

In December 1936, the secretary of the nearby Adfa District Nursing Association, Mrs Thomas of Castell, Adfa, wrote to the Llanfair Association, asking if Nurse Mills Evans could do duty for them as they had no nurse. It was not until March 1938 that a formal arrangement was made by splitting the Adfa district between the areas covered by the Llanfair and Tregynon Associations. This gave Mam additional formal responsibilities for the Dwyrhiw, Llanllugan and Cefn Coch communities but, in reality, this was work that, already, she had been covering for some years. In 1938, also, another awkward boundary dispute arose concerning the area served by the Llanfair and Meifod Nursing Associations. This was not eventually sorted out until December 1943!

The first mention of a superannuation scheme for district nurses came in 1937. Discussions as to whether Nurse should become a member next arose in 1941, and my mother entered the scheme in 1942. The Rushcliffe scheme, which brought increased financial obligations on local nursing associations, was adopted in 1944. In consequence, the Llanfair Nursing Association came under new pressures with the need for greater financial resources and expenditure. The Rushcliffe scheme had increased salary scales for nurses and there was a further increase in 1945. Thus, it became necessary for the Llanfair Association to raise more money locally by organising flag days on the streets, asking for increased donations from local people; and, also, by raising the fee for Nurse's attendance at child birth cases from £1. 10s. 0d (£39.11p) to £2. 2s.0d (£54.75p). Because my mother had been covering, for some years, the area served by the Upper Banw Nursing District Association, it was suggested that the grants paid to that Association should now be paid to the Llanfair Caereinion Association but the officials serving the Montgomeryshire County Nursing Association refused. Issues concerning nursing cover and provision for the Upper Banw Association were never resolved. When all nursing associations were finally wound up with the arrival of the

National Health Service on July 5 1948, the former Upper Banw District was merged with that of Llanfair Caereinion.

The Minutes of the Llanfair and District Nursing Association provide us with interesting insights into the numerous small but essential costs that had to be met. In 1941, it was agreed to provide Nurse with a new outer coat and the local tailor, Mr David Astley, was given the task of making it. After numerous enquiries as to progress, two years later, in 1943, it eventually turned out that it would be necessary to purchase the coat from another source. Presumably, under war-time conditions the tailor was unable to obtain suitable cloth. In 1937, there is the mention of the need to provide a telephone for use by Nurse. This was discussed again in 1938 when it was suggested that a line extension could be run from the local chemist's pharmacy (Preswylfa) across Bridge Street to our home. The extension was never provided but a separate line was eventually installed in 1940, and now Nurse could be contacted, at any time of day or night, on her own phone number, Llanfair Caereinion 50.

To my knowledge, Mam never took a holiday and this is revealed in the minutes kept by the Nursing Association. In June 1934, it was recorded 'Nurse Evans should take a holiday when most convenient'. And, again, in 1939: 'Nurse Evans has not yet taken her holiday but has not complained. It was left to her and the Secretary when she was prepared to take them'. Then, in 1946, there occurs the stark statement: 'It was agreed to write a letter to Nurse Evans on her recent success and also urge her to go for treatment and take a rest. It was also hoped that Nurse would soon be quite well again'. The congratulations related specifically to my mother having become the first nurse in Montgomeryshire to be awarded the Certificate for the Use of Gas and Air Analgesia Apparatus, following her examination at St Mary's Hospital in Manchester.

In July 1942, the Llanfair Nursing Association decided, wisely, as it turned out, to start a reserve fund by investing in War Savings Certificates. Later, in February 1947, details of a special meeting concerning finances is recorded in the Association's Minutes. This involved key members of the Association's Executive Committee meeting the manager of the Midland Bank, in Llanfair Caereinion, to discuss an overdraft amounting to £104. The signatures of two guarantors were required. It was agreed to surrender the War Savings Certificates and Mrs Milton Jones, the wife of Dr Walter Milton Jones, our local GP, who worked closely with my mother, generously provided an interest free loan of £75. In addition, to cope with this financial crisis, the Upper Banw Association was further requested to make extra subscriptions so that liabilities could be met.

Although no specific annual reports are available for the communities of the Upper Banw, at this time their local nursing association was administered by Mr Pierce Roberts, the Treasurer, a stalwart of the community, who was the headmaster of Llangadfan Church School 1902-46. In the Llanfair annual report for 1946-47 the sum of £63.3s.3p (£63.16p – the equivalent of £3,019.93p today) is recorded as having been collected for the Association. The Secretary was a Mrs Arthur, the wife of David John Arthur, who ran a bus service to Llanfair from the communities of the Upper Banw Valley. The rules and fees for the Llanfair Association, which seemed to have been printed in the early 1920s, are included in Appendix A. Often some of these were ignored, as from my own knowledge I know that Nurse Mills Evans never refused anyone a visit for whatever reason.

As mentioned earlier, typical examples as to the format and content of the annual reports published by local nursing associations, including lists of subscribers, are reproduced in the Appendices. The first covers the year 1917-18, but this was published before my mother had commenced her duties in Llanfair (Appendix B). The second is for 1921-22 (Appendix C). By this time mother had taken up her post as the District Nurse for Llanfair and surrounding communities. The third report included in Appendix C, for the year 1946-47, is very interesting because it covers the year immediately before the National Health Service had come into existence and before the NHS had taken over all health responsibilities throughout Montgomeryshire. This latter report marked the end of the local nursing association and therefore must be regarded as an important local record in its own right. Each of these reports contains the names of the Association Committee, sometimes a general account on the work of the District Nurse, a finance statement, together with names and amounts of money collected from local residents in house-to-house collections and the names of the collectors.

For collection purposes, the area covered by the Association was split up into various districts. In the 1917-18 report twelve districts are recorded but, in the last report for 1946-47, the number of collecting districts had been expanded to twenty-one. The Upper Banw district, including Y Foel, Llangadfan and Llanerfyl, must have had their own house-to house collections but there are no extant records of these. From the annual report year ending 31st March 1918 (Appendix B) subscriptions and donations amounted to £23.3.3 (£24.18p – equivalent to £575.89p today); patients' fees amounted to £11.14.6 (£11.72 – £279.46p in today's value); whilst Nurse's annual salary was £78.00 (£1,859.07 in today's value).

Some interesting items include £2.4s.3d (£2.21p) for bicycle repairs, £1.10.00 (£1.50p) for the hire of the main hall in the Public Hall and Institute at Llanfair Caereinion for a concert which raised the sum of £29.7.0. (£29.35: £699.53p in today's money).

In addition the following receipts are recorded:

Table I: Grants and Awards to Llanfair and District Nursing Association, 1917-18

Llanfyllin Guardians	£ 2. 2. 0
Education Authority Grant	£10. 0. 0
King Edward Memorial Fund	£ 5. 0. 0
Health Visiting Grant	£ 5. 0. 0
Castle Caereinion Charity	£ 1. 0. 0
Total	**£23. 2. 0 (£233.10p)**

Nurse Gethin was the District Nurse at this time (Figure 4) and it is recorded that during the year she dealt with the following patients: medical 20, surgical 17, maternity 9, tuberculosis 3, which necessitated a total of 555 home visits. In her capacity as Health Visitor, 176 visits were made, with some 29 visits to elementary schools in the district, when 101 children were inspected, and a further 76 children were visited in their homes. The total number of visits to all cases amounted to 1,169 in 1917-18, compared with 1,215 during the previous year. There is also a note stating that several of the midwives holding appointments were then about to retire on the account of their advancing years and, as a consequence, work on maternity cases was increasing greatly.

In the annual report for the year ending March 31st 1922 (Appendix C), when mother was the District Nurse, the following items are noted: major donations and subscriptions for the year amounted to £17.1.6 (£17.7½p); subscriptions obtained through house-to-house collections amounted to £42.8.0 (£42.40p); collections in places of worship, £3.14.4 (£3.71p); and patients' fees, £33.19.6 (£33.97½p).

The nurse's annual salary had now been increased to £100.13.0 (£100.65p – the equivalent of approximately £3,600 in today's values). Other interesting items include £11.00 for a new bicycle. In retrospect this sum appears to have been extremely high (the equivalent of £390.62 in today's money) because, in all probability, bicycles were then hand made and they only became cheaper when they began to be mass produced in the 1930s. For the first time the accounts report the purchase of a uniform for the Nurse; a medical bag and cupboard were included in the payments. During the year Nurse attended the following calls: medical 21, surgical 20, maternity 38, tuberculosis 7, which necessitated a total of 1,436 home visits. In her capacity as Health Visitor, some 194 visits were made, including 25 visits to Primary Schools and 64 visits to children at home. The schools visited included the Board and Church Schools in Llanfair; schools in Llanerfyl; Hafod; Y Foel; Llangadfan; Pont Robert; Dolanog; Llangynyw; Rhiwhiriaeth; Cwm; Pantycrai, and Dwyrhiw. The total number of visits was 1,436 in 1921-22 compared to 1,078 the previous year. In addition, a number of grants were received (Table II).

Table II: Grants and Awards to Llanfair and District Nursing Association, 1921-22

Nurse's Salary Augmentation	£10. 0. 0
Health visiting	£10. 0. 0
Local Education Authority	£12. 0. 0
Welsh National Memorial	£ 5. 0. 0
Board of Guardians	£ 2. 2. 0
Castle Caereinion United Charities	£ 1. 0. 0
Ministry of Health	£ 4. 0. 0
Total	**£44. 2. 0 (£233.10p)**

The report for 1921-22 contains an appreciative note: 'Nurse

Mills is most energetic in her work and deserves every appreciation'.

In the annual report for the year ending March 31st 1947 (Appendix D), the following items appear: major single subscriptions for the year amounted to £4.4.0 (£4.20); house-to-house collections £81.3.3 (£81.16p); collections from places of worship £3.15.0 (£3.75p); from the Upper Banw Association £63.3.5 (£63.16p). Mrs Milton Jones, the wife of our local doctor, had provided an interest free loan of £75. The Nurse's own salary for the year amounted to   £376.12.0 (£376.20 – about £8,680 in today's value).

Some interesting expenditures are recorded in the accounts: for example, a car allowance and the hire of tractor during snow totalling £64.5.3 (£64.26p – £1,481.73 in today's money). 1947 was one of the harshest winters experienced, with extremely heavy snowfalls – hence the need for tractor hire. Also in the report occurs a telephone account for £13.19.9. (£13.98p – £322.52 in today's prices.

On the receipt side appears a sum of £2.00 for the sale of equipment from the First Aid Post (this had probably been put in place during the war years when the First Aid Post was in the Institute). There was also a sum of £1.17.6 (£1.75p) by balance of commission on rose hip collection arranged Mrs Hopkin Jones, the wife of the then Vicar of St Mary's Parish Church in Llanfair Town. Rose hips were collected in great numbers to help the war effort and were used for increasing the supplies of Vitamin C in the form of rose hip syrup. As usual, various sums came into the local nursing association funds from a number of different sources (Table III).

Table III: Grants and Awards to Llanfair and District Nursing Association, 1946-47

County Nursing Association	£ 37. 0. 0
County Council Infant Life Protection	£ 1. 10. 0
Education Committee School Nursing	£ 13. 10. 0
Welsh National Memorial Association (Tuberculosis visiting)	£173. 15. 2
Mileage grant	£ 58. 4. 8
Telephone grant	£ 5. 0. 0
Castle Caereinion Charities	£ 2. 0. 0
County Council (General Account)	£ 22. 5. 0
Total	£318. 4. 10 (£318.24p)

The report for the year ending March 31st 1947 also recorded that Nurse attended the following cases: maternity 27 (involving 378 visits), medical/surgical 70 cases (involving 970 visits). Nurse also made 435 visits as a Health Visitor and to see tuberculosis patients. The total visits for all cases amounted to 1,783 for the year. Some 53 visits were made to schools in the area and 81 visits were made to the homes of children.

It was also reported that the County Nursing Association had indicated willingness to assist and co-operate in carrying out the provisions of the new National Health Act 1946. The usual appreciative thanks were extended to Nurse for carrying out her work efficiently and conscientiously.

Nurse's visits to schools were to control nits infections found in the hair of young children. Only one pupil had to be affected and soon the nit infestation spread like wildfire to all others. The nits were dealt with by combing them out from washed hair, whilst still wet, onto a plate, using a fine-bladed steel comb, and then they were killed. I used to enjoy these visits because Mother always gave me a sweet. Nonetheless, this didn't stop me from having nits in my own hair from time to time!

The final meeting of the Llanfair District Nursing Association took place on June 3 1948, prior to its functions being taken over by Montgomeryshire County Council. There is no doubt that local district nursing bodies, such as that serving Llanfair Caereinion and its rural hinterland, could not have continued much longer due to the demands for higher nursing standards against a continuing serious shortage of funds.

With the arrival of the new state National Health Service in July 1948, so ended an era of house-to-house collections. Everyone had been committed to the cause of providing the nursing and midwifery service to Llanfair Caereinion and district, not only the hard working committee and the dedication of the house to house collectors but also the commitment and generosity of the Llanfair people themselves who ensured that a qualified nurse and midwife was always available.

CHAPTER THREE

The District Nurse in the Rural Community

In the sparsely populated district surrounding Llanfair Caereinion, with its great expanse of rough terrain and many remote houses, the journeys that Nurse had to make were not easy. The general lack of electricity supplies for domestic purposes, and my mother's love-hate relationship with her means of transport, provided many hair-raising and amusing incidents – to us, at least. Despite the difficult conditions, the delivery of so many babies under such hazardous circumstances was remarkable.

Although having little or no fear of driving, and with no knowledge of anything mechanical, in reality, Mam was a very poor driver. Not that she thought so! Mother hated driving and, whoever was actually at the streering wheel, had to drive to *her* speed and follow *her* instructions. When Margaret, my first wife, was setting out for Newtown to take her driving test, mother quite earnestly and seriously told her to tell the driving examiner that the Llanfair District nurse had taught her to drive. We all thought that this information, in itself, would have resulted in her failing the driving test!

Like all other pre-war drivers, Mam had never taken the driving test. Like the majority of people at that time, she much enjoyed a cigarette. When we lived in Bridge Street, in Llanfair town, it was the duty of one of the family to park Nurse's car outside the house, facing in the 'right' direction, ready for her to jump in and set off on her nursing duties. All our neighbours always knew when Nurse was leaving. With her cigarette in her mouth, to take off she would rev the engine up unmercifully and then shoot off at a speed not exceeding 25 miles per hour. Wherever she was going or whoever drove her, anyone exceeding that speed would be shouted at and told in no uncertain terms to slow down. My brother John recalls that mother rolled her own cigarettes from Ringers A1 Tobacco but whenever he accompanied her on her nursing duties – perhaps to lay out a dead person or attend a confinement – she would take a nice leather cigarette case containing five Craven A cigarettes for herself and five Senior Service cigarettes for John to smoke. She would never smoke in other people's houses – only in the car on the journey to and fro.

On one occasion she was driving up Neuadd Lane, the narrow road out of Llanfair town, which passes the entrance to the High School. This country road is still very narrow today, with not enough room for vehicles to pass each other. Unfortunately, on this occasion she met a local farmer coming in the opposite direction in his car. The following exchanges took place: Nurse: 'I'm sorry Mr Jones, I'm afraid I can't reverse'. Mr Jones: 'Neither can I Nurse, bech [bach]'. The outcome was that they had to walk back to the farm and find a farm labourer to reverse one of the cars. Another fear, apart from speeding, was what mother called, in Welsh, 'goriwaereds'. This was her word for hillside roads and tracks with an unfenced drop to one side, and she had a lifelong fear of making a mistake in her driving and going over the edge. To counteract this in the only way she knew, mother would take a sheet of newspaper and wedge it into the wound up front window on the driver's side. By not being able to see the offending drop she could pretend it wasn't there and this gave her a little more confidence as a driver!

However steep or however narrow the road, mother would never turn back when out on call. I cannot recall a single instance in all the years, despite inclement weather and vehicles breaking down, when she failed to get to see a patient. When all else failed, she would walk.

If there had been a heavy fall of snow and mother had been called out, and if the distance was too far to walk, my brother or I would be sent to Mr Parkes, who kept horses at the Coach House in the New Road in Llanfair town. We were told to ask if mother could borrow the horse. He never refused and in a very short time the horse, ready saddled, would arrive outside our house. Mr Parkes never charged for this service, such was his generosity and his appreciation for Nurse's work. I can remember that there were three horse mounting blocks in Llanfair town: one was by the Black Lion Inn and that is still there; another was located at the top end of Watergate Street near by Dolgron Cottages (now the site of the Wynnstay Farmers Depôt). The third horse mounting block was sited at the bottom of Watergate Street, opposite the Wynnstay Hotel (now converted into private flats).

From 1923 onwards mother owned several motorcycles. The first of these had a belt to drive the wheels before the days of the chain. It was on such a machine that my father taught Nurse to drive on a straight stretch of the main road just outside the town. Mother was standing astride the motor-cycle with my father standing alongside giving instructions. Whatever Mam did is not clear but when she revved up the engine the machine shot off by itself, leaving her standing on the road. Another mishap with a motorcycle was attributed to my father. He had fitted a sidecar to the machine to enable us to travel about together as a family. On one of the first occasions he tried this out, thankfully he was by himself. The motorbike and sidecar were parked outside our house in Bridge Street, facing down street, and my father tried to turn it around in one sweep to go back up street. The result was that the sidecar mounted some steps leading to the house opposite and the whole thing toppled on father. Fortunately, he escaped unhurt.

For a very short period in the early 1930s a Bean motor car was purchased. This had a canvas top covering only the driver and the front seat passenger. In the rear, in what was known as 'the boot', was the dickey seat. When the door of the boot was lifted, two seats appeared. My brother and I would sit together in these seats open to all the elements.

On April 29 in 1933 a report appeared in the local newspaper, *The County Times*, reporting that mother had been involved in an accident. She had been riding her bicycle in Llanfair town when she was knocked down by a motor cyclist, Mr Eric Davies, landlord of the Prince of Wales public house situated near our home in Bridge Street. It was reported that her hands and face were injured but that she was progressing satisfactorily.

It was much later that driving tests became compulsory; so, mother never did have to take a driving test. Despite the thousands of miles she drove, often in treacherous conditions and, despite her noticeable lack of driving skills, Nurse was never involved in any major accidents. One day, however, as she was driving to Cefncoch she accidentally ran over and killed one of a pair of courting pigeons. On further daily visits along the same road, for several days, the remaining pigeon could be seen looking for its mate. The sight of that lone pigeon upset mother very much. It is surprising that a member of the nursing profession could get so upset about this lone pigeon.

One particular mishap that confirmed Nurse's fear of driving occurred on the night that she attended a confinement in a house with the local doctor, an ex-naval surgeon commander who was rather fond of his whisky. On the return journey home mother was the passenger in the doctor's car when the ring of the steering wheel came off in his hands. The doctor simply put the ring around his neck and steered the vehicle home by means of the protruding spokes! Mother walked into our house shaking, and looked extremely frightened. The doctor just accepted a glass of whisky and left.

It was the same doctor and mother that I drove to a

40

confinement on a snowy winter night to a remote dwelling. The two previous children of the expectant mother had also been born during the winter months. So, while Nurse was upstairs preparing for the birth, the doctor sat in front of the fire downstairs, drinking the father's whisky, and admonishing him for having failed to ensure that his children should have been born during the summer months. My brother, too, had a hair-raising experience with this same doctor. The birth of a baby was some days overdue, the home was rather remote and it was dark, and the expectant mother had to be taken to hospital rather quickly. So, she was put in a wooden, high-backed chair and carried manually across the fields to the car. The doctor was urging my brother to drive faster and faster over the rough roads. The healthy baby was born within a few minutes of their arrival at the hospital.

In the majority of cases when nurse was attending a confinement she coped on her own. If she thought that the birth was going to be difficult, or if the woman's previous deliveries had given problems, Nurse would take a doctor with her. As a young boy I would often accompany my mother on her nursing duties. In the early 1940s, being the only one at home, no doubt I was regarded as good company by my mother. But, in truth, I was also very useful for opening and closing farm gates of which there were many. Sometimes, as many as four gates had to be passed through before we reached the farmhouse. Cattle grids had still not been heard of in those days.

It was on such an occasion that one dark, stormy winter night we were approaching Llanfair, returning from duty. The headlights of the car were covered by the war time regulation masks, giving a very poor light. An old lady from Llanfair, who was walking in the same direction, with her head bent into the storm, turned into the path of our car as we approached and she was knocked down unconscious. I was petrified. We lifted the old lady into the front passenger seat of our two-door vehicle. Mother wanted me to sit in the rear seat and hold the old lady up to stop her from slumping forward. This I refused to do. Instead, I did agree to stand on the running board on the driver's side and, leaning across my mother, kept the unconscious woman upright in her seat. Eventually, we did manage to get the old lady into her own home, where she lived alone. We made her comfortable in an armchair downstairs and then went to the police station to report the incident. By the time mother and the police sergeant returned to the old lady's house she had locked the door. Either she could not, or would not, open the door, refusing to answer their calls. We were all very concerned about the old lady's condition, so a ladder was brought to the scene to reach her open bedroom window. The police sergeant went up the ladder and enquired through the open window if the occupant was 'all right?' This polite enquiry was met by a tirade of abuse from within and the matter was not taken any further.

On another occasion I had accompanied Mam when she went to 'lay out' a dead body. This is the term used in the nursing profession for preparing someone for burial, immediately after death. District nurses were not obligated to render this service and some district nurses refused. Mother never refused to undertake this important final act of service and kindness. On this occasion there had been a heavy fall of snow and the house where she had to carry out her duties could only be approached by a very steep lane. Mother would not allow me to gather any speed to approach the snow-covered hill. In consequence, our car started to skid. Mother insisted on walking up to the household to carry out her important duties. This gave me the opportunity to reverse to the bottom of the hill and, without mother, I could now approach the climb with as much speed as possible. I was quite pleased with myself when I managed to get the car up to the house and turned it around ready for the descent. Much to my dismay, when mother completed her duties, she insisted on walking to the bottom of the hill, a distance of about a mile. I was quite hurt that my efforts had not been appreciated, but, as anyone who has ever driven under such difficult conditions will know, going down a hill is much more dangerous than going up!

One of the hardest winters I can recall was that of 1947. In some places around Llanfair there were snowdrifts of nine to twelve feet. It was during this time that Nurse received a call to another confinement in the Cefncoch area. By a stroke of good fortune a caterpillar tractor was leaving Llanfair town with a load of fodder for the sheep in that district. Mother insisted on a ladder being brought. With great difficulty, and some help, she managed to get herself on top of the trailer loaded with the fodder, even though some of the men tried to discourage her. That is how she travelled, complete with her black bag, to preside at a successful deliverance of a new baby. In those days cars did not have any internal heating. No matter how many miles we travelled, the inside of the vehicle remained stone cold. So, on one of our vehicles, my father, being a plumber by trade, ran a copper pipe inside the cab. This had been fitted to the radiator of the car, enabling hot water to circulate through the copper piping, thus providing some heat for the cab. These pipes did, in fact, get quite warm but the heat they gave out did not seem to make much of an impact on the low temperature inside the vehicle.

One of the last places I recall going out to with Nurse was, once again, to lay out a dead person at Christmas time. The farm house was in Cwmtwrch, a narrow valley above Y Foel. There had been a heavy snowfall, and, to make matters worse, there was a severe frost. Even so, we did manage to get our car a fair way up the valley. A local farmer had come to meet us on his Fordson Major tractor. These were not fitted with a cab, so, to reach our destination, mother and I had to sit on the rear of the tractor, wrapped in hessian sacking that was in use before the plastic bags. In the days that followed the weather deteriorated further. It was over a week before the coffin could be carried by tractor and trailer down to Y Foel for burial.

On another occasion a man, who had been taking the role of Father Christmas in a local school, had died still wearing his Father Christmas outfit. For some reason nearly twenty-four hours elapsed before Nurse was asked to attend. When we arrived at the school, in the company of an elderly local gentleman, we discovered that the school caretaker, who lived in the adjoining school house, had gone away and had taken the school keys with her. Being the youngest and smallest, I managed to break in through a partly-open window and eventually I was able to let the others in. 'Father Christmas' was lying on a polished wood floor and, at the first attempt to disrobe him, he slid around and a foul smelling substance trickled from his mouth. At this, I ran outside and spent the rest of the time being sick, hanging over the school railing. I was unable, indeed unwilling, to help any further.

For a long time afterwards I was teased unmercifully about this episode which had ruined my Christmas and New Year celebrations. For many days after, I could only smell that terrible smell and that, coupled with not being accustomed to seeing death, has had a lasting effect on me. It was some time later, when our family firm of painters and decorators was carrying out the external painting of the Newtown Hospital, that I refused to paint the doors of the morgue because there was a dead body inside. Some of the other painters also refused to carry out this work. But one of the older painters put this into proper perspective by commenting ' . . . It's the living that you should be afraid of, not the dead'!

It was my brother, who was much braver than I, who took mother, accompanied by the police, to cut down a man who had hanged himself. Some days after this tragedy Nurse was accused, by the dead man's wife, of stealing his pocket watch. The police confirmed that Nurse was innocent of this accusation. I can recall another sad event concerning a man who had not been about for some days. Eventually, he was seen through the kitchen window, sitting in his wooden armchair, in front of his fireplace; but the man had been dead for some days. Just in case foul play had occurred, the police were called. Because this man had lived alone, the house was in somewhat a mess. The only place to lay him out was on the kitchen table and this proved a difficult task for my mother and my brother, as the man had died in the sitting position.

During the war a number of aircraft did crash in our district (see Doylerush, 1993). When Nurse was making regular daily visits to a homestead called Neintirion, situated in the hills at the top end of Cwm Nant yr Eira, near Talerddig, a Lancaster bomber crash-landed and pieces of the aircraft were spread over a wide area. A small fighter plane also crashed on top of Moel Bentyrch, Llanerfyl. I can recall the wreckage of the aircraft being recovered by a team from the Royal Air Force. The remains of the fuselage were loaded onto a recovery vehicle that was parked for some time at the entrance to the town's Deri Woods (Coed Derw). All the town's residents must have paid the wreck a visit, with the local youngsters clambering all over the aircraft remains, looking for bits to be kept as souvenirs.

A lady from the Dinas Mawddwy area used to visit mother at home in Llanfair regularly for medical treatment. Her farm was situated in a remote part of the Cader Idris range of mountains. She told my mother that a couple of aircraft had crashed on their upland pastures but these were never recovered because the area was too remote and inaccessible. As far as I am aware, the remains of these planes are still there on the mountainside.

On July 22 1944, Nurse delivered a baby girl, to be named Ceinwen, to Mrs Elsie Davies at Pantymilwyr, Rhiwhiriaeth. A week later, she was returning home from a visit to see the new mother and baby, when an American fighter-bomber crash-landed in a nearby field near Penycroenllwm House. Nurse's first instinct was to run to the crashed plane in the hope of saving life. The tangled wreckage was burning furiously. Because of the heat, ammunition was exploding all around and for that reason Nurse could not get anywhere near the cockpit of the plane. Unfortunately, the pilot had been killed. This upset Nurse a great deal although, under the circumstances, nothing could have been done to save the life of the young airman.

Fifty-eight years later, on Sunday July 28 2002, an inscribed marble plaque in memory of the young pilot, Second Lieutenant Arthur Guy Jenkins, Junior, of Phoebus, Virginia, USA, was unveiled at Rhiwhiriaeth Community Centre – just across the fields from the site of the crash. On July 28 1944, the plane was on a training flight. It had emerged from cloud at low level and the pilot decided to turn steeply to avoid a house. In consequence, his plane crashed into the ground. He had been a member of the 495th Fighter Training Group, based at Atcham, southeast of Shrewsbury. The memorial plague was unveiled by Major Irvine 'Dusty' Miller, the Commanding Officer at Atcham in 1944, who now lives in retirement in East Anglia (Figure 3). Others amongst those at the dedication ceremony included David Jones, the last surviving member of the Llanfair Caereinion Air Observer Corps (see Pryce, 1991, 27, 172), who had tracked two P47 Thunderbolt Fighter planes travelling up the Banw valley but only one returning; Sydney Watkins of Penycroenllwm, the farmer's son who was one of the first on the crash scene; and Michael Heath, representing the American Military Cemetery at Madingley, Cambridgeshire, where the young pilot is buried. The baby girl, whom Mam had delivered, is now Mrs Ceinwen Williams; and she lives with her family at Pantygelynen, Llanfair.

Just before the outbreak of World War II in 1939, a local sixteen year old girl, Nancy Marsh, who was brought up at Red House, Llanfair by her grandparents, was left homeless when both died within a month of each other. As there were no known relatives, Nancy came to live with us and for a number of years our house was the only home she knew. Mother introduced her to the nursing profession, arranging for her to start at a hospital in Brentwood, Essex. She became a nursing sister in the Army

Nursing Service and regularly came home on leave. Mother always maintained a room for her. She married Robin David, then an officer in the army, who later became a judge, now retired, who was knighted by the Queen in 1995. Lady David, or Nancy, as we always knew her, died in December 1999.

I have often wondered if my mother would have loved to have had a daughter of her own. Every time we accommodated anyone new in our house invariably they were always girls. What convinces me even more about this are some very old photographs that I have of my father, mother, brother and myself. I am shown in a dress – though I have been told that during the early part of the century it was common practice to put dresses on very young boys (Figure 6).

Over the years, in her role as nurse, mother was often approached by young girls, or their families, for information on joining the nursing profession. Mother did all she could to help them realise their ambition and quite a number of them remained in nursing. Unlike today, nursing was then considered to be a calling, and attitudes of caring were much more important than academic qualifications. Much to mother's dismay, and, indeed, to that of all members of our family, a letter appeared in the local newspaper condemning the fact that the Nurse was going about her duties not wearing a uniform. The local newspaper received a large number of letters, many of them were printed, in response to this criticism. These not only defended her professionalism but were full of praise for the challenging and difficult work that she did. I can recall many instances, which demonstrated the inappropriateness of the standard lightweight uniform and regulation shoes issued to nurses. These were completely inappropriate for the nursing duties carried out in upland rural communities by my mother.

On one extremely stormy night the Nurse was called out at a late hour to a confinement in a remote farmstead. The long lane approaching the farm was crossed by a small brook. The small brook was in flood and swift flowing when we reached it.

The water level was above our knees and it was impossible to drive the car through the torrent. This did not deter mother who always seemed well prepared for such emergencies. She tied her nursing bags around her neck and, with the aid of a stout old walking stick, which was always carried in the car, she waded through the swollen brook as the car headlights lit the way. After leaving the car and me, she still had half a mile to walk to the farm where she was to deliver the baby. I was ordered to return home.

The 'nursing bag', as we always called it, was essential when Nurse went out on duty, and especially when she received an emergency call out. At some period, probably just after the end of the war, Nurse went on a course to learn how to administer gas and air during painful confinements. Thereafter, for child birth cases, two bags now had to be carried around, the latter, known as the 'gas bag', accommodating the new equipment.

The Montgomeryshire Health Authority eventually appointed a new Chief Nursing Officer who, on her appointment, wrote to all district nurses in the County, informing them that she intended to visit them once a month. She intended to travel out into the local district with the Nurse and to check that all nursing records were kept in good order. On one of her first visits to Llanfair it was unfortunate that mother was making daily antenatal visits to an extremely remote farmstead, situated to the far west of Cefncoch, almost to Carno. The farm could not be approached by car and could only be reached by walking a mile or so across windswept moorland. It was a wet and miserable day, so mother decided to take the new Chief Nursing Officer to Gorsdyfwch. Unfortunately, the visiting official was clad in the light nurse's raincoat and high-heeled shoes. After walking along the rough, muddy terrain for a short distance, the Nursing Officer conceded defeat and beat a hasty retreat back to the car. She never visited mother again to check on her rounds! Gorsdyfwch, which is now deserted, was one of the last places that nurse visited where the people could

Central Midwives Board.

1 Queen Anne's Gate Buildings,

Westminster,

London, S.W. 1.

 APR 192

Madam,

I have to inform you that you have satisfied the Examiners at the recent Examination, and that your name has accordingly been entered on the Midwives Roll. A Certificate will be prepared and forwarded to your enrolled address in due course.

Yours faithfully,

H. G. WESTLEY,

Secretary.

Miss *H. E. Mills*

Fig. 1. *Formal notification of registered status of Nurse Mills Evans as a Midwife, 1921.*

Fig. 2. *Montgomeryshire district nurses attending a midwifery course at Gregynon Hall, Tregynon, 1923. Nurse Mills Evans is shown, kneeling, in the front row (right). The man with the beard is Dr Owen Morris, the County Medical Officer for Health.*

Fig. 3. *Major Ervin 'Dusty' Miller, the Commanding Officer in 1944 of the US Air Force 495th Fighter Training Group, based at Atcham, Shrewsbury, who, on Sunday July 28 2002, unveiled the memorial tablet at Rhiwhiriaeth Community Centre to Second Lieut. Arthur G. Jenkins, Jnr. The young pilot of the American P47 Thunder Bolt fighter plane was killed outright in the crash at Rhiwhiriaeth on July 28 1944. Nurse tried to help on her return journey home from seeing her patient at Pantymilwr.*

Fig. 4. *Nurse Pricella Gethin,*
c.1918. Nurse Gethin was the
District Nurse and Midwife
for Llanfair Caereinion before
Nurse Mills Evans.

Fig. 5. *Nurse Mills Evans and her two sisters, Annie Mills Boorman (school*
teacher in Manchester) and Jane Evans Owen (nurse and midwife, and
formerly Mayoress of Llanidloes), outside Buckingham Palace,
after Nurse had received the MBE on March 5 1957.

Fig. 6. *Nurse Mills Evans (my mother), Idwal Evans (my father), with my brother John (left) and the writer in my customary dress, c.1929. In the late 1920s most men smoked. My father was no exception to this general trend.*

Fig. 7. *Mr Fred Jones, grocer, scout master and an early member of Plaid Cymru, with my brother, John, 1937. Together they went on a fortnight's hiking trip throughout northern Wales. For the start of their journey my father took them in his car to the top of Bwlch yr Oerddrws, on the mountainous road west of Dinas Mawddwy.*

Fig. 8. *Much of my father's work was done in collaboration with other craftsmen. Here he is shown with members of a former well-known Llanfair bulding firm, 1937. The photograph was taken outside Nantlle House (on the site of the former Swan Inn): Front row, left to right: Thomas Evan Jones (father of Heber Jones); John Jones, Caerbellan (skilled craftsman and a giant of a man, known as 'Long John' to everyone); and John Lloyd Jones (brother of Thomas Evan Thomas); Rear, left to right: Heber Jones, builder; Evan Morgan, Idwal Evans (my father).*

Fig. 9. *A former water cistern in cast iron, supplied and fitted by my father. Stop tap covers in the streets bearing my father's name appeared after c.1930, when he installed the first domestic water supplies for households in Llanfair town.*

Fig. 10. *Members of the first Fire Service Brigade at Llanfair Caereinion on fire-fighting exercises at Dyffryn, Meifod, c.1940. The Brigade was part of the A.F.S. (Auxiliary Fire Brigade), later known as the N.F.S. (National Fire Service). Wearing uniforms, left to right: Bob Thomas, Hassal's Square; Evan Morgan, Melin-y-ddôl; Jac Jones, Institute Cottages (controlling the hose); Cyril Tudor, Tanyfron; Dick Thomas, Institute Cottages; Jack Ralph, Hassal's Square; D. Idwal Evans, Bridge Street – all residents of Llanfair town.*

Fig. 11. *Scout troop, outside the Wynnstay Hotel, Llanfair Caereinion, c.1938. Front row, left to right: John Martin, George Cross, Donald Astley, Emyr Davies. Second row: Andy Ridell, Tommy Evans. Standing, in the rear, left to right: Mr Henshaw, Church School House, scout master; David Mills Evans (the author), Billy Evans, with Arthur Billington (behind, white shirt).*

Fig. 12. *Serious flooding in Bridge Street, Llanfair Caereinion, September 1958.*

Fig. 13. *Row of concrete defence blocks from World War II, used to reinforce a wall in the storage area behind the former shop of Morgan Bros, Bridge Street, Llanfair Caereinion, September 2001.*

Fig. 14. Llanfair Caereinion Platoon, 5th Battalion Montgomeryshire Home Guard at Henarth, Llanfair Caereinion, 1945.

Front row, seated, left to right: Davies, banker; John Williams, Pentalcefn; Ted Evans, Melinyddôl; Tom Jones, bus driver; Dick Huxley; John Lewis, Peartree; John Jones; Albert Hewitt, head master, Church School.

Row 2, also seated, left to right: Meirick Watkin; Ivor Williams; Jack Hughes; Harry Roberts; Bert Astley, teacher; Fred Jones, grocer; Cadwaladr, Midland Bank manager; Heber Jones, builder; Dick Evans, Gwynyndy; Johnny Williams, Goat Hotel.

Row 3, standing, left to right: Robert Davies; Emrys Watkin; Edwin Williams; Selwyn Blover; Tommy Evans; Emrys Owen; Owen Owen; Percy Thomas, Bytack; Emlyn Evans; Lloyd, Tanfron; Jackie Owen.

Row 4. Standing on left, left to right: Ieuan Williams; Arthur Thomas.

Row 4. Standing on right, left to right: Ted Leary, baker; Peter Davies; Will Richards, Llanoddion.

Row 5 (back row), standing, left to right: Tom Jones; Tommy Jehu; Willie Watkin; Vincent Jones, grocer; Vic Threadgold; Ivor Williams, Tan House; Edwin Williams; Roberts, Dolfarddyn Fach; Percy Thomas, Cwmllwyngwyn; Joe Jones, Rhydllechan; Sidney Watkin, Nantwyllt; Tom Jones, Graig; John Benting, Creuaden.

Fig. 15. *Improvement work on the culvert for Nant-y-Bwt and Nant Cafnant in Bridge Street, Llanfair, 1934-35.*

Fig. 16. *Drainage improvement work in Bridge Street,
Llanfair Caereinion, c.1934-35, showing, left to right, Maldwyn House,
Paris House and, on the extreme right, Rathbone House, our retail shop
and house. The boy shown on the crossing planks is my brother
John Mills Evans. Also shown: Harry Phillips (man, standing),
Jane Roderick (woman in mid distance and mother of Mr Phillips).
The son of Mr Phillips, George Phillips, in his eagerness to join
the army, gave a false age. He was killed in World War II.*

Fig. 17. *World War II Nissen hut at Heniarth, Llanfair Caereinion, September 2001. This is the sole remaining of three such huts that once accommodated a fully manned search-light battery.*

Fig. 18. *Flooding in Bridge Street, Llanfair Caereinion, September 3 1958. The strong force of the flood waters shifted this three-ton lorry down the street from the Market Square (shown in the middle distance, right).*

Fig. 19. *The flooded premises of Morgan Bros., ironmongers and general merchants, lower Bridge Street, Llanfair Caereinion, September 3, 1958.*

Fig. 20. *Interior damage due to flooding at Morgan Bros, ironmongers and general merchants, Llanfair Caereinion, September 3, 1958.*

Fig. 21. *Afon Banw in flood near Melin Dolrhyd, September 1999.
The submerged track for the Llanfair Light Railway lies beyond
the fence posts protruding above the waters.*

Fig. 22. *Afon Banw in flood, 1999. The photograph shows
the view looking upstream towards Melin Dolrhyd.*

Bridge Street: east side

William Jones & Sons, Old Bank House, *grocers;*

Watkins, The Emporium, *newsagents and fancy goods;*

Fred Jones, *grocer;*

Morgan, Victoria House, *tailors and men's wear;*

W.H. Davies, Birmingham House, *shoe shop and Farmer's Co-op Agent;*

Ivor Annwyl Evans, Liverpool House, *Milliner and children's clothing;*

W.B.W. Metcalfe (later E. Maendy Jones), Preswylfa, *pharmacis;*

Mrs Pain Jones, *sweet shop;*

Jane Ann Edwards, *sweet shop;*

Morgan Brothers, Bridge End Store, *ironmongers, agriculture merchants etc.*

Bridge Street: west side

David Astley, Paris House, *tailor;*

Mills Evans, Rathbone House, *paints and wallpapers;*

Maureen Tanner, Rathbone House, *hair dresser;*

Mrs Peate, Cartrefle, *shoe shop;*

Bill Roberts, Star Shop, *clock and watch repairs, sweet shop, Pearl Assurance Agent;*

Empson Davies, Empress House, *ladies and gentlemen's hairdressing;*

Mr George Hughes (later Mr Roberts, blind man?), *sweets and ice cream*

Victor Thomas, Manchester House, *draper, clothing and knitting wools;*

Blodwyn Jones, Holly House, *fish and chip shop;*

Williams, Brook House, *temperance hotel;*

Francis, Bridge House, *tea shop and letting rooms.*

Fig. 23. *Retail businesses in Bridge Street, Llanfair Caereinion late 1930s-1958.*

Menu

Cocktail di Scampa

Essenza Madrilene in Tazza

Filetto di Bue Perigourdine

Biscotto Diaccio Sasa al Grand Marnier

Panieri di Frutta

Saffe

Music before and during the Banquet by the
Orchestra Casina delle Rose

Fashion Parade arranged by La Gregoriana

Fig. 24. *Banquet menu for the International Conference of Midwives,*
Thursday October 6 1960, at the Palazzo du Congressi of the E.U.R., Rome.

GET RICH QUICK LIMITED

Dear Nurse Mills,

Knowing you to be a cute business woman, I am placing before you a most wonderful business proposition and shall be glad if you will let me know per return the amount you are willing to subscribe towards the formation of the Company.

The object of the Company is to operate a large cat ranch to start, in which we should have 50,000 cats, each cat averages about 12 kittens a year which would give us about 600,000 skins. These skins sell at about one shilling each making our annual revenue £30,000 or roughly £575 per gross per week.

A man can skin fifty cats a day for £3 per week; so that we should require 32 men to operate the ranch, making a net weekly profit of £450.

The ranch will be self supporting as the cats will be fed on rats. For this purpose, we shall start a ranch for rats on the adjoining land, commencing with 50,000 rats which multiply four times as quickly as cats, giving us four rats per day per cat. The rats will be fed on the carcasses of the cats from which we have taken the skin.

Hoping you have got the idea and awaiting your reply.

Yours etc. Good Will

Fig. 25. *Joke letter received by Nurse Hannah Mills, my mother, prior to her marriage in 1923.*

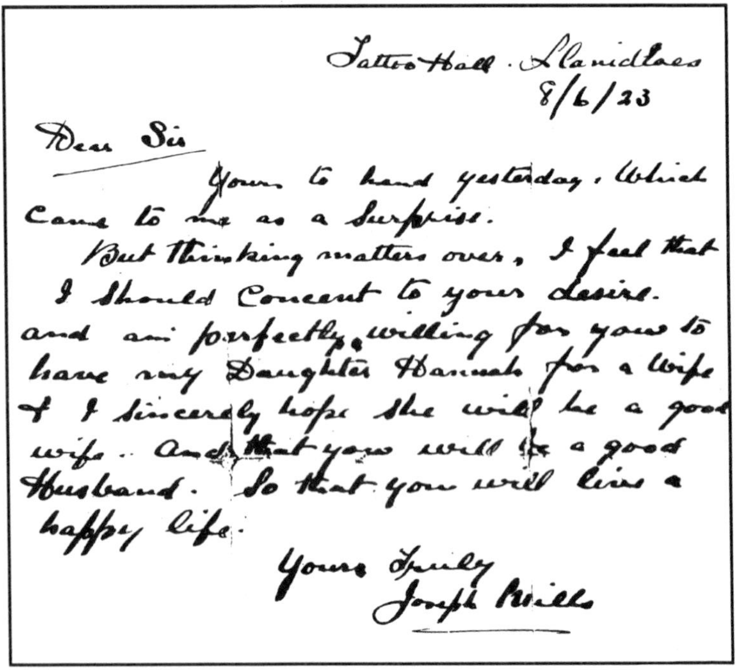

Sattre Hall. Llanidloes
8/6/23

Dear Sir

Yours to hand yesterday. Which came to me as a surprise.

But thinking matters over, I feel that I should consent to your desire. and am perfectly willing for you to have my Daughter Hannah for a wife & I sincerely hope she will be a good wife. And that you will be a good Husband. So that you will live a happy life.

Yours truly
Joseph Mills

Fig. 26. *Personal letter to my father, Idwal Evans of Llanfair Caereinion, from his future father-in-law, Mr Joseph Mills of Llanidloes, June 1923, in reply to his formal request to marry his daughter, Nurse Hannah Elizabeth Mills, my mother.*

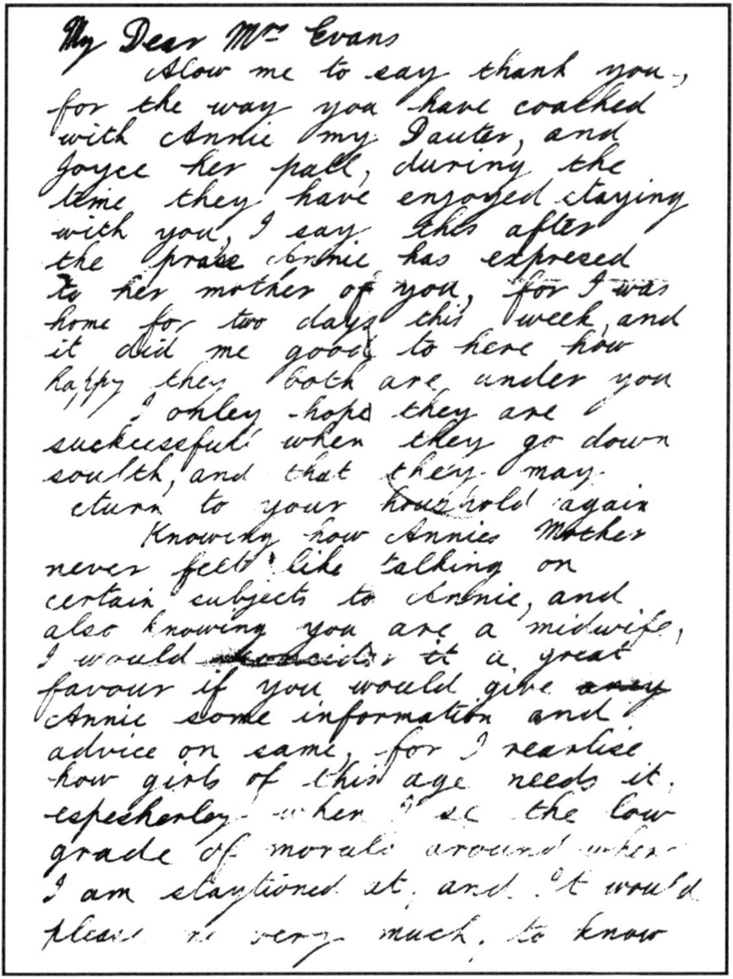

My Dear Mrs Evans

Alow me to say thank you, for the way you have coalked with Annie my Dauter, and Joyce her pall, during the time they have enjoyed staying with you, I say this after the prase Annie has expresed to her mother of you, for I was home for too days this week, and it did me good to here how happy they both are under you I ohley hope they are suckuseful when they go down soulth, and that they may eturn to your houghold again

Knowing how Annies Mother never felt like talking on certain subjects to Annie, and also knowing you are a midwife, I would consider it a great favour if you would give away Annie some information and advice on same, for I realise how girls of this age needs it especherley when I se the low grade of morals around when I am stationed et. and it would please ri very much. to know

Fig. 27. *Letter to Nurse Mills Evans from a 'Mr H. Jones', c.1942.*
Mr Jones is thought to have been a native of south Yorkshire, serving in the army. It seems that this letter to Nurse had been enclosed with another letter to his daughter, who was then living with the Mills Evans family in Llanfair.

. there is some one close at hand
to Annie, dropping a word of
advice now and agen, for
I think every girl would apreceate
such, not that I have aney
doutes as regards to Annie, but
a word in time, saves much
pain later on, not onley to
Annie but to aney girl. She
in turn may inform same, and
who can tell where She may get
to, and what work She in time
may do, perhaps your profeshion
in another country, for this war
is certainley chainging costoms
quick.
      Hopeing this short note finds
you in good helth and happy
and that your husband is well
or much better, and a happy
remunion in the near futcher.
            cherio bye and thanks
again
            Yours
                Mr H Jones.

Fig. 28 (*continued from page 67*)
Letter to Nurse Mills Evans from a 'Mr H. Jones'.

converse only in Welsh and were unable to speak English. The head of the household carried the bardic name *Alaw Llugan*.

There were many such remote dwellings in the district served by mother. Nurse paid regular visits to a dwelling near Llyn Hir to deliver new babies. The house was situated by the side of the lake in the hills between Cefncoch and Llanerfyl. Today, it is unoccupied and has been so for many years. The place sticks out in my mind because there were four or five gates to open and close on the approach road; and always it was my job to open and close them, going, as well as returning.

Of course, not all mother's work was carried out in farmhouses on stormy windswept moors. On some occasions, time was of the essence and the saving of life was more important than the clothes that mother happened to be wearing when she was called out. The nearest blue baby unit was situated in Birmingham but, over the years, especially after the war had ended, mother delivered a number of such babies. She would think nothing of putting the baby on the rear seat of the car and delivering it directly to the unit in Birmingham. When we remember her none too good driving skills, this was, indeed, an achievement!

Mother herself, suffered from Drinking Diabetes *(Diabetes Insipidus)* and her craving for something to drink became so acute that she would consume up to two bucketsful of water in a matter of hours. But, she was no alcoholic! The nearest that mother ever came to alcoholism was the odd spoon of whiskey in her cup of tea! Eventually, mother needed proper medical treatment and she was fortunate to be acquainted with a local man who was a surgeon in the Liverpool Northern Hospital. On the journey to the hospital Mam insisted on driving, taking with her two buckets of drinking water that she had placed on the floor behind the driver's seat, with a tea cup at hand, so that I could give her a drink, when required. At last, we set off for Liverpool at the usual speed of 25 mph, stopping occasionally for a drink of water. When we reached the dual-carriage way between Chester and Liverpool, our speed did not increase, even though she was driving in the fast lane. A lorry driver, overtaking us on the wrong side shook his fist at us and shouted 'You're not fit to be on the road, woman'. Mother's response was that she was the Llanfair Nurse. She had paid her motor taxes and therefore she was allowed to drive anywhere at her own speed. Worse was to come. Immediately after we had come out of the Mersey Tunnel, we were not quite sure how to find the Liverpool Northern Hospital. In the middle of a five-road junction stood a policeman, busily directing traffic. Of course, mother had to get out of the car and ask him directions. He was not pleased!

After a short stay in hospital, for the rest of her life mother had to sniff Piton powder up her nostrils and this curtailed her drinking habits. At the time we travelled to Liverpool the short dual carriage way consisted of just two lanes either way. This was regarded as something of a wonder for drivers from rural Montgomeryshire: in fact at that time, the only set of traffic lights in the whole of Montgomeryshire were those in the centre of Welshpool.

Mother's illness did not deter her nursing at all, nor any of her many activities. She took it upon herself to organize the local blood transfusion collection. Prior to the service coming to Llanfair, she would inform as many donors as she could of the arrangements and ensure that they had the means to attend the sessions for the donation of blood. She booked the public hall in Llanfair's Institute, ready for the event; and she organized the tea and biscuits that every donor received afterwards. My brother and I had to ferry the donors in from the outlying districts: from as far afield as Y Foel and Meifod; and then, afterwards, we had to return them home. When we finished all this ferrying of people each of us was then expected to give blood as well!

When my first wife was learning to drive, often she was taught by Mam as she went about her nursing duties. They received a call out to a young girl who, living with her grandmother, was experiencing severe pains. On arrival at the house, it was discovered that the girl was about to give birth. Both the girl and her grandmother were unaware of her pregnant condition and, consequently, nothing had been prepared for the event. After the baby girl was delivered she was placed in an emptied sideboard cupboard, lined with a sheet and wrapped in a white silk scarf. Despite everything, the child was very healthy.

The county health authority ran a scheme whereby a grant of £14 was given, in some instances, to provide clothing for the new born. In the granting of approval for this small award the Nurse's discretion was probably the major criteria; and Nurse always fought very hard for this concession.

The money was never given directly to the parents but was handed to Nurse who would deposit it in a local clothes shop where the parents would be sent to select the clothing. This is yet another example of ways in which people supported each other in our community. Nurse could have retired at the age of sixty but, instead, she chose to continue as the 'Llanfair Nurse'. Our family had purchased a seaside house at Fairbourne, on the Mawddach estuary in Meirionedd, in preparation for her retirement. Dad had moved there permanently but mother's heart was in Llanfair. If she was not expecting any midwifery cases, she would go, reluctantly, to Fairbourne on a Saturday evening but would return home to Llanfair on the Sunday morning, after she had been to the Welsh service in the local chapel.

In 1957, the New Year Honours List included the name of my mother in recognition of her services to nursing. This came as an unexpected honour for her and the volume of congratulatory telegrams, telephone calls, letters and people calling at our house was phenomenal. Among the many telegrams was one from the County Health Headquarters at Newtown which read: 'MBE, More Babies Ever. Heartiest congratulations and good wishes'. There was a letter from a retired Penarth Chapel Minister living in Cardiff, offering congratulations with an addition 'well done, Nurse – well deserved'. A lovely letter, also, came from Jane. E. Thomas, a Welsh Regional Nursing Officer, based at the Temple of Peace and Health in Cathays Park, Cardiff. She commented that she was a Montgomeryshire person herself, and that her own home had been at Y Wig Smithy in Dolanog. A congratulatory letter from Bethesda, mother's own chapel in Llanfair, emphasized the community's appreciation: 'We are very proud indeed but we remember with gratitude the magnitude and quality of the services you have rendered the country and for which you have been justly awarded'. Another letter came from a gentleman in Birmingham who had attended Manledd School at Y Fan, Llanidloes, with my mother so many years ago. He had read in the newspapers that Nurse ran two cars in the event of one breaking down. After his congratulations, the letter read: 'You certainly fully deserved it more appropriately than a mountebank [i.e. a charlatan] who is so well paid chasing a bit of inflated leather across our football pitches; and footballers make the awards cheaper than the Sunday School Medals which are given to children as a rule. You lucky girl, having two cars; I remember Lord Davies using two cars!'. True, Mam did own two cars, but that was just in case one of them broke down. In this way she ensured that her important nursing duties could always be carried out.

On 5th March 1957 Nurse was invested as a Member of the British Empire (Civil Division) by the Queen at Buckingham Palace. There was much discussion as to who should accompany her to the investiture. My father, my brother and myself were somewhat reluctant to go. So, it was Nurse's two sisters who accompanied her (Figure 5). For some time after the receipt of the MBE there was quite a demand for mother to address branches of the Women's Institute and similar meetings on her nursing career. On one such trip mother's driving skills and her mechanical knowledge – or, rather, the relative lack of them – were, once again, made apparent. Mam had left home by car to give a talk to a Women's Institute some miles away. She had not been gone more than twenty minutes when the telephone rang. The car had broken down, and mother informed us 'The big end has gone'. I took another vehicle and delivered mother to the meeting in the local village hall to give her talk. Of course, I was invited into the hall and spent between two and three embarrassing hours with the kindly ladies. On the return journey home, we stopped to inspect the broken-down vehicle. The only problem with the car was that it had a flat tyre!

When the New Year's Honours List was first published, there were congratulatory letters, also, from the Minister of Health, the Welsh Board of Health, the Minister of Welsh Affairs, and a telegram from the editor of the *Nursing Times*. But the one letter that gave mother the most satisfaction was from Mrs Hewitt, Secretary of the Women's Institute in Llanfair Caereinion. It was dated 5th. January 1957; and, in congratulating Nurse, the Llanfair WI invited her to be their guest of honour at their New Year Party. Recently, I met a lady from away who had lived for some years in Llanfair. When her first daughter was born, my mother arrived at the confinement dressed in her fur coat. The birth of the baby girl and the WI's New Year party had occurred the same evening. So, I can only assume that, in the end, Nurse had missed the celebrations.

CHAPTER FOUR

A Family of Painters and Decorators

Mother married father in 1923, my father being one of the sons
of Evan Owen Evans, painter, decorator and glazier. Before her
marriage, Mam received a letter from H.V. Bowen, the founder
of Bowen's Quarries, at Tan-y-foel, Cefncoch, a family firm still
in operation. It was a fun letter and I believe that such letters
were popular at the time (Figure 25).

Without a doubt, similar humorous letters would be
frowned on today; but in the past such messages were written
and sent in a tongue-in-cheek way – especially amongst young
people of marriageable age. Letter writing was much more
usual in the previous century. Indeed, the personal letter was
the main means of communication before the full development
of the public telephone service. Figure 26 is another interesting
example. This was written and sent in June 1923 by my maternal
grandfather, Joseph Mills, of Tattoo Hall, Llanidloes, to my
father who had asked for Nurse's hand in marriage. Evidently,
my father was regarded as acceptable to the Mills family.

There is no doubt that father's family had lived in Llanfair
for several generations. There was a person recorded as 'Evans,
painter' in Broad Street in the town back in 1850 but it is not
known if he was an ancestor. Several members of my family can
be seen in the old photographs reproduced in *The Photographer
in Rural Wales* (Pryce 1991). My grandfather, Evan Owen Evans,

is shown wearing his painter's apron. And again, on page 158 (Pryce 1991, Figure 5.6.3) there is an old photograph, dated c.1910, showing my uncle, C. Bernard Evans, who stands with his workmen in lower Bridge Street, Llanfair, close to his trade signboards, advertising his painting and decorating business. That particular photograph had been taken from across the street, outside the dilapidated buildings that were demolished later to provide the site on which the town's new Institute and Public Hall was built (opened in October 1913). This was a time when, as impressive new buildings were put up in Llanfair, new craftsmen were attracted to work in the town. In 1912, when the new building for the North and South Wales Bank (later the Midland Bank) on Llanfair's market square was nearing completion, a Tom Morris of Vrongate, near Westbury, in Shropshire, arrived. He was an artisan joiner, brought in to work on the heavy wood fittings and elaborate counters inside the bank. He then went on to contribute his skills to the completion of the new Institute in lower Bridge Street, being responsible for making and fitting of the splendid oak panels in every room throughout the impressive new building. During his time in Llanfair he met and married Minnie Evans, my father's sister. Later, they went to live in Birkenhead where he continued his skilled trade, fitting out luxury cruise liners at the Camel Laird shipyard. When eventually he retired, they returned to live in Llanfair at Dolerw, in Watergate Street.

A footpath to the right of the old buildings, near the paving fence shown in the picture reproduced in Pryce (1991, Fig. 5.6.3, p.158), led from Bridge Street into the parish churchyard; and this passed two or three cottages, known later as the Institute Cottages. Our family rented an old building (a former flannel factory) beyond these cottages, where we stored our supplies of paint, glass, tools and general equipment (including the all-important sets of ladders). Later on, my father purchased the old Malt House on Mount Road for storage purposes and to use as a garage for our vehicles. This building was demolished a few years back and the site is now used as parking for the Spar grocery shop nearby. Originally, this former three-storey building had been used to dry hops and make beer for the Black Lion public house opposite.

Until it was demolished, some of the old malting equipment was still there – including the old fire tiles, perforated with small holes, on which the hops would have been dried by air rising from the fire lit underneath. There was also an old wooden shovel used for turning the hops.

Other old things, which for some time have been thought to be of little value, included a huge bath with heavy brass fittings. This had been removed by Dad from the manager's home at the Midland Bank in Llanfair. It was the first bath with running water ever to have been fitted in any house in the town. There was also a pane of frosted glass taken from the front door of the former Prince of Wales Inn (now known as Windsor House) in Bridge Street. This had the three feathers emblem and the words 'Prince of Wales' etched into the glass.

Other items included old carbide bicycle lamps, the round and square bevelled glass panes used as replacements in carriage lamps, chandler's equipment for the making of candles and many other relics now, sadly, lost for ever. Carbide, however, was used for other purposes than the production of acetylene gas for lighting purposes. We used to put carbide in a tin, put the lid on tightly, making a little hole in it. The interaction of the carbide and the water mixing caused an explosion, and some poachers were known to use this as a fishing technique. The fish would have been stunned by the explosion and could then be easily collected. My brother still owns a piece of plate glass on which is inscribed ' E. O. Evans, Painter, Glazier, 1882'. This belonged to my father's father. When he died he left £10 to each of his children but he left the business to his youngest son, who was unable to cope with the paperwork needed to run a successful business. So, my father purchased the business from his brother with his £10 share out.

In 1936 my father won the contract to supply Llanfair town with the first drinking water supply to individual homes (Figure 8). The main supply was stored in a huge earth-covered tank, covered in grass, which can still be seen at the bottom of the steep Gibbet Hill on the B4389 road to New Mills and Manafon. For many years, the manhole covers in the streets of Llanfair carried my father's name. All that is left displaying his name today is an old cast-iron lavatory cistern, now used for growing flowers (Figure 9). Until that date, but in some homes for a considerable period afterwards, people would carry their water in buckets from communal taps strategically placed around the town. These public water taps had a door-knob type handle which you had to keep turned clockwise to start the flow of water, but if you released this knob, the water stopped.

I can remember the location of every one of these community taps. One was opposite Astley's motor garage in Pool Road and people living in the nearest houses had to cross the main road to get their water. Another was at the bottom of the footpath (known as 'Crickety Crock') linking Neuadd Lane to the town, located directly opposite Llanfair bridge, at the side of Dolgoch Cottages. The next one was at the bottom of Parson's Bank, by the former shop of Morgan Brothers. Another was in Duck Street, just off Bridge Street, between Paris House and Rathbone House. A fourth water tap was fixed in the stone wall in Mount Road, opposite the former Bee Hive Stores (now the Spar shop). A fifth supply point was to be found nearby in Wesley Street. In the other direction, there was the sixth tap opposite Swan Yard, a seventh opposite the Post Office, in High Street, with an eighth tap at the far end of High Street, beyond the Top Town (Top Llan) Chapel (Capel Ebeneser). The ninth and tenth public water-supply taps were in Watergate Street. But some households retained their own wells and there was a well in the field behind the Bridge Garage in New Road. Dr Milton Jones (senior), our local GP during my younger days, always used this well for his drinking water. Before these public taps had been installed, water had to be raised directly by hand pumps from one of a number of wells in Llanfair. There was one such well in the middle of Hassall Square and another in the rear approach lane to the houses in Bridge Street, whose back entrances start opposite the Black Lion Inn.

During World War II my father served as the Leading Fireman in the local Auxiliary Fire Service Corps (Figure 10). The headquarters of the fire brigade was a large Nissen Hut in the field opposite the Mount Field (the town's football ground). Today, private houses stand on the site. The fire station's equipment included an American Packard vehicle to tow the fire fighting appliance. This was capable of moving at speeds exceeding 100 miles per hour – something unheard of in vehicles at this time. Llanfair Fire Brigade's American Packard tow lorry was a vehicle of much local admiration. One of the earliest callouts the local Fire Brigade attended was the barn fire at Tanllan Farm (about half a mile outside Llanfair on the Welshpool road). The water to fight the fire was drawn from the River Banw, a good field's length down below. The pump was not strong enough to lift sufficient water up the steep incline. So a second pump was installed half way up the field, thus boosting the supply to fight the fire. Unfortunately, when the fire was eventually under control, and the order came to switch off the pumps, the pump in the field was switched off, but the pump by the river continued pumping, causing many of the fire hoses to burst. Another memorable fire, which took some days to control, occurred on land beyond Dolmaen, some 12 miles west of Llanfair, on the main A458 road towards Mallwyd, where, in past generations, peat was dug from the ground. Using fire beaters, rather than water, was the only way in which this serious fire could be brought under control.

CHAPTER FIVE

The War-time Years

Whether or not it was because I was now older and more aware of them, the biggest changes appear to have occurred after the outbreak of war in 1939. Until then, mother worked continually as the District Nurse and Midwife, except when she was giving birth to my brother and myself. Her sister Jane, who was a qualified nurse and midwife in Llanidloes, was present at both confinements and also carried out duties on behalf of mother on those occasions. When I was born on December 22nd in 1928 preparations were in hand for Christmas. Mother had been confined to bed, so my aunt and my father were left to prepare and cook the Christmas goose (turkey was not in fashion in those days). The goose was too large to fit into our oven, so they decided to saw the bird in half. Mother was not too pleased. At this time most households did not have the facilities to roast Christmas poultry. Sc, for a small fee, many people took their prepared bird to the local bakehouse, where it was cooked ready for collection by mid day. The vegetables were all prepared and cooked at home.

Llanfair's animal slaughterhouse was another sort of communal kitchen. This was situated in the buildings behind Empress House, just off the Market Square. Bones from the animals that had been killed were put into a large boiler and simmered away for hours to produce a broth sold to townspeople for a few pence. Usually, this broth was collected in carrier cans (similar to the well-known Australian billy cans).

Frequently our whole family would be invited out for afternoon tea, usually on a Sunday. Teatime was always at about 4pm and generally consisted of tinned fruit with bread and butter, butter and jam spread on bread, and home-made cake. The tea was served in the best china cups. Lemonade was not readily available, although I do recall a small lorry coming around on odd occasions selling Corona lemonade and fizzy drinks. Going out to tea was, indeed, a big occasion for which we were all dressed up in our best Sunday clothes. My brother and I would have been to Sunday school in the afternoon. Later the whole family would be going to evening services at Bethesda, the Wesleyan Methodist Chapel in Llanfair. Before leaving home the instructions were always the same: 'Eat bread and butter with your fruit. Only take one piece of cake. Say "Please" and "Thank you". Otherwise, don't speak unless you are spoken to'. Grace was always said before the meal. Tables were laid with a beautiful white cloth and the fears of dirtying this cloth were an added worry. Nonetheless, we were pleased and grateful to be asked out to these teas. One of the regular homes to which we were invited was that of Mrs Williams, Corner Shop. Long demolished, this stood in Watergate Street between the former Wynnstay Hotel and No. 1 High Street, the shop of Mr Frank Twist, saddler (see Pryce 1991, p. 135, Fig. 5.3.2). After Mrs Williams, this shop was run by John Lloyd Astley (my grandmother's brother on my father's side). 'John Lloyd', as everyone knew him, was a clock and watch repairer who also sold cigarettes and sweets, was a barber, and ran a sideline as a bookie. Emrys, the son of Mrs Williams, had been an officer on the Fyffes' banana boats before the outbreak of war. But during the war these ships carried more vital equipment. Unfortunately, his ship was torpedoed and he did not survive. His name can be seen on the Llanfair's war memorial in the High Street.

From the outbreak of war until after 1945 bananas were generally unavailable. Ice cream was something else that was in short supply, although even before the war it had been far from plentiful. Two or three evenings during the summer months, usually on a Saturday, an ice cream van would visit Llanfair. The van, owned by a Mr Brown of Oswestry, resembled a four poster bed! He rang a hand bell to announce his arrival in the town.

My father, who employed a number of painters, ran our family business. Before the war he was awarded the contract for the external painting of a large number of council properties in Welshpool. An entry in one of our old ledgers shows that the accepted price was £7 10s (£7.50p – the equivalent of £369 today) per dwelling. The actual costs of the materials used were greater than the cost of the labour; this trend continued until some time after the end of the war. A top tradesman could earn in the old currency, 4d (1½p) per hour, brush hand 3d (1p), and labourers 2d (1p) – worth 82p, 62p and 41p per hour, respectively, in today's value.

Just before the outbreak of war in 1939 my father suffered a serious illness from which he never fully recovered. This left mother with many added responsibilities and a greatly increased workload which she tackled with her typical hard work and enthusiasm and discovered an acumen for the family business – hitherto untapped. In 1938 a new vehicle had been purchased, an Austin eight horsepower car, registration number BUN 938, complete with a set of snow chains to fit over the rear wheels. These enabled the car to climb the steepest hills when they were covered in snow. But we considered that these chains did considerable damage to the vehicle itself and, moreover, the ride was anything but smooth. Rock salt had not yet come into use for keeping roads open in wintertime; consequently, fresh snow was pressed down hard by the continual flow of traffic. Often, the hard-packed snow had been frozen and thus it would remain on the roads for many weeks. These conditions made for dangerous driving – even on the flattest length of road. The only response from the local council was to spread chippings on the steepest stretches of road. Incidentally, this particular car had been purchased from a Mr Davies who ran a small garage in Berriew. The same firm now trades as 'W. R. Davies (Motors)' from larger premises in Salop Road, Welshpool.

It was during this pre-war period that mother was returning home from duty in the hills around Cefncoch when in the distance she saw a large glow of light in the sky. She arrived home in quite a nervous state. The following day she discovered that the glow was caused by the Airship R101 which had gone up in flames over northern France. The year was 1930.

Cefncoch, its people, and the surrounding hills, were always strong favourites for Mam. Even though the terrain offered some of the wildest countryside in her district, mother retained great respect for everything about this locality and its community. When I was a boy occasionally she would take me out for a picnic. The venue was always the same: the other side of Cefncoch, towards Y Rhyd, on the exposed country road leading westwards from Llanfair Caereinion town to Carno. Just beyond the turning for Bowen's Quarry this remote quiet country road was little more than a cart track that finally petered out. After the war, with the increase in road building, the quarry owners improved this as a through road all the way to Carno, thus cutting the cost of transporting their stone to western districts of Mongomeryshire. At the time of writing, this area is now being considered as a site for wind turbines for the production of electricity.

Because of Dad's poor health, mother had to take an interest in the running of the painting, decorating and plumbing business, in addition to her responsibilities as District Nurse and Midwife. The war did not help matters: firstly my brother, and, later, I was called up to join the armed services.

One of the first changes at the outbreak of war was the influx of evacuees to rural areas and Llanfair was no exception. Being the local nurse, mother was one of those responsible for finding homes for these poor, unfortunate children. Those allocated to Llanfair, in the main, were pupils of Saint Francis Xavier's School, Liverpool. They came from an impoverished inner city area and many had never seen the countryside before. To add to the problems, the evacuees were of the Roman Catholic faith – something of which the people of Llanfair knew little or nothing. How could anyone house, with any success, children with a different religion, culture and upbringing? Like many other parts of rural Wales, Llanfair was, overwhelmingly, chapel, and dominantly protestant in faith. It was a sorry sight to see so many young evacuees in strange surroundings, wondering what the future held for them. One or two mothers came with them to see their children settle down. The fathers had been called up into the armed forces or, since they came from a major seaport, many were already serving in the merchant navy.

The evacuees arrived with their gas masks slung over their shoulders in little cardboard boxes. Most wore pumps (plimsolls) – totally unsuitable for wearing in the hard winters that we normally experienced. Today, heavy snowfalls seem to be a thing of the past: a six-inch covering of snow used to be commonplace and a pair of stout boots was a necessity. Very few people owned a pair of Wellington boots and at the time I cannot recall any being manufactured for children. Many local farmers wore leggings made of leather but certainly these were more prominent on fair days and funerals. They always appeared to have been so highly polished.

When they first arrived, one of the things most sought after by the evacuees was a fish and chip shop, a service which, at that date, did not exist in our town. For many years the late Mrs Blodwen Jones – known to everyone as 'Blod Chips' – cut, fried and sold chips on two or three nights of the week from her home, Holly House, in Llanfair's Bridge Street. A pot of peas was always simmering on an open fire at Holly House and some people brought eggs, which she fried for them. Many of the townspeople would take a bowl and it would be filled with chips, be covered by a cloth and taken home to be eaten as supper. Thus, Blod's fish and chips was an early form of a fast food take-away.

Many of Llanfair's people had never travelled far from the town, so they did not easily understand some of the ways of the evacuees. The annual church or chapel Sunday school trip to the seaside was the greatest distance most of us would have ventured by the early 1940's. An amusing incident occurred in an apple orchard owned by a Mr Hughes then living in Ivy House on the New Road. The orchard, whose site is now part of the forecourt to the Bridge Garage, was opposite his house, at the bottom of Neuadd Lane (the lane leading to the High School). The newly arrived evacuees decided to help themselves to Mr Hughes's apples but he caught them in the act and shouted at them, 'Put those apples back'. The evacuees responded by actually trying to replace the apples back on the tree! The Roman Catholic background of the evacuees, with their different attitudes and behaviour towards the keeping of Sunday as a day of rest, also gave rise to some problems. How could the inhabitants of a small quiet Welsh country town, where no one worked on Sunday, who dressed in their best clothes on the sabbath and went to chapel or church three times, cope with young children running riot, playing football and in generally creating much noise? On the other hand, it must be stated here that circumstances were equally difficult for the evacuees. Their lives had been turned upside down, too. We did not understand their city ways and, in those days, perhaps we were not as tolerant as we would have been today. Some of the evacuees stayed on after the war ended: they married girls or boys from our locality and they, and their families, still live in our community. Several have remained very true and loyal to those who took them in; these former evacuees have continued to visit Llanfair and have remained in touch with their original hosts. Early in the war years for a short time Mam took in two evacuees. But, like a few others of them, these children preferred life in the big city, despite all the air raids, to life in the country. They did not remain with us for long.

In the early years of the Second World War there were five well-attended places of worship in the town: St Mary's Parish Church, Annibynwyr (i.e. Independent), Baptist, the Calvinistic Methodist and the Wesleyan Methodist Chapels. There was no animosity between these different places of worship but, at that time, to us the Catholic Religion and its ceremony was indeed very foreign. The Baptist Chapel was the first to close in the early 1940s. Since then, the building has had numerous uses: functioning as a canteen for school dinners, accommodating an egg packing station, a storage depot for a farm supply company, a textile processing factory; and, latterly, the building has been tastefully converted into a private house. The Wesleyan Chapel was finally demolished in 1983 (because the end wall was unsafe) and a private house now stands in its place. Some of the pews and interior furnishing were given to the Baptist Chapel at Newchapel, Dolwen (near Llanidloes) when it was refurbished after serious fire damage. One of the leading members of the Baptist movement in Llanfair during the 1940s was the well-known Mr Freddie Jones. He kept a grocer's shop in Bridge Street, Llanfair. Fred was a passionate supporter of Welsh culture and an early activist on behalf of Plaid Cymru (see Pryce 1991, pp. 78, 153, 154). Among his many other interests was involvement with the Scout movement, long-distance hiking, and he organised and ran a Boy Scout Troop in Llanfair (Figures 7 and 11).

During the early 1940s everyone had to carry a gasmask wherever they went. Even schoolchildren had to take their masks to school with them. For babies and toddlers, the fitting and distributing of these masks was the responsibility of the District Nurse – mother. Gas, having being used during the First World War was a great fear and a distinct possibility. The masks for young babies were large, ungainly contraptions that resembled what we would now know as a space suit, with a large 'window'. Straps were tightened at the bottom to make the whole thing gas proof. The baby was placed inside, head first. On the side was a concertina type hand pump for producing a supply of clean air into the mask via a filter. Toddlers' masks were more conventional and these were slipped over the head, with adjustable straps. To make them more appealing to children, these masks were finished in bright colours with a funny floppy nose for breath extraction – known as Mickey Mouse masks. Another of Nurse's responsibilities was the distribution of National Dried Milk, concentrated orange juice and cod liver oil. The Government supplied these free for babies and young children, but they were available only in exchange for official coupons. Very often Nurse would take these products on her rounds and distribute them. People calling in our family shop to collect these products also bought other goods – thus increasing sales. There were drawbacks too. On many occasions people requiring these goods would be knocking on our door up to, and, sometimes, well past midnight.

During the 1940s a number of traditional customs were still carried out on special occasions in Llanfair town. Following a wedding in one of the chapels it was the custom for young unmarried people to stretch a rope across the road, so preventing the passage of the newly-married couple. After a token payment the wedding party was allowed to proceed. One of the oddest customs I recall took place at a funeral at Llanwddyn. After the burial, the gravedigger would wait by the cemetery gates holding out his shovel on which the mourners put money. This paid for his services.

In Llanfair town, if a funeral cortège passed up Bridge Street, you can be sure that all the householders would have drawn their curtains across their windows as a mark of respect. Even the roller blind on our shop window was unrolled. Of course, the blind would always be down on a Sunday as were those on all shop windows in Llanfair. If one happened to be a pedestrian on the street as the cortège passed – as I remember on one occasion in company with my father – men doffed their hats and stood with bowed head until the procession had passed. Even when driving a car, signs of respect for the deceased were made. If a driver met a hearse followed by a number of cars then he would pull the car to one side and switch off the engine as a sign of respect. Such traditional ways of showing respect for the dead dies hard. Even today, at the sight of a funeral, I feel I should do something. When my father passed away a few years ago, his elderly sister did not switch her television on for a week.

During the war years every village and town had a body of men which, when first formed, were called the Local Defence Volunteers. The LDV, recruited from members of the older generations and those unfit for military service, was formed to support the army in the event of an invasion. When first started the LDV had to train with broom handles in lieu of rifles. Soon, however, they were supplied with standard army 303 rifles, complete with bayonet. The LDV – sometimes jokingly referred to as the 'Look, Duck and Vanish' – were later renamed the Home Guard. Many of the members were ex-servicemen of the First World War (Figure 14).

When eventually the Home Guard was issued with rifles, they were stored in a cellar room in Bridge Street under the Calvinistic Methodist Chapel (Moriah). The access door to this store led directly on to Bridge Street. The man in charge of the rifles and ammunition was himself an old soldier, Mr Fred Jones, mentioned earlier, who ran a grocery shop in Bridge Street. The following hitherto unpublished extracts from the autobiography of Fred Jones record details of the formation and early history of Llanfair's Home Guard:

The Second World War, 1939-45

. . . One of the first five to join up in the Home Guard were myself and

Garfield Astley, enrolling at the same time at the Police Station. Having got under way, Mr R.D. Hughes was appointed in charge, under him was Mr Sam Henshaw, he having served in the First World War, and later in charge was Mr Gilbert Davies, MC, the solicitor from Welshpool who remained with us until we were disbanded. When the necessary stores were coming through, blankets, clothing, ammunition and fire arms, grenades etc., I was placed in charge [having] been given the rank of Quarter Master Sergeant. Later I was promoted to Lieutenant Quartermaster and with this rank I finished.

Llanfair and District Section of the Home Guard consisted, or was made up of the following Platoons:

Y Foel: in charge, Emlyn Rees;
Llangadfan: in charge, Thomas John Francis
Llanerfyl: in charge, Harry Roberts;
Dolanog: in charge, Plenydd Gittins;
Heniarth: in charge, Williams, Delfryn;
Cefncoch: in charge, the Vicar, the Rev. William Morris;
Castle Caereinion: in charge, Bert Astley;
Llanfair Caereinion: Cadwalader (Midland Bank Manager).

All eight held rank of Lieutenant. Foot drill was carried out partly in the Institute and up the New Road. Arms drill and instruction on the firearms was carried out in the Institute, firing on the Range at Castle Caereinion, bombing at Allt y Gadair, outside Llanfyllin, Sunday being the day set aside for both these operations; First Aid instruction [was conducted] in the Institute. Exercises on a big scale were carried out at Llansantffraid and at New Bridge, Meifod; Bridgeman, at the close of the last named, commenting on our failures. In charge of the 5th Montgomeryshire Home Guard was Lieutenant Colonel C.F. Meade of Penlan Hall, Meifod. Our Adjutant was Miskin, stationed at the Drill Hall, Llanfyllin, and [he] was assisted in his work here by Jones of Dolwar Fach now Clerk to the Llanfyllin Rural District Council. Ac yr oedd yn lwcus iawn ohono ['And we were lucky for that'. In his writings Mr Jones often broke into Welsh which was his first language].

It now comes to my mind that a number of us went on a course down to Winchelsea [East Sussex]. This was most instructive. Those that I call to mind were: Lieutenant Johnny Bowen, Sergeant Richard Evans; Edwards, Rhosgall; Mike Watkin, Walad Jones and myself. Strange to say, in charge of the canteen was the Duchess of Bedford who later was missing in a plane accident over the North Sea, a lovely personality and was extremely fond of Welsh singing and often came down to Wales (Barmouth). The Officer in Charge at Winchelsea was an Olympic runner. While stationed here our bombing planes were very active over the French coastline making several runs a day (24 hours) preparing for the opening of the Second Front.

On one occasion the Llanfair Home Guard was called out late on a moonlit summer night. It was suspected that German parachutists were descending on the hills above Llanfair. The Home Guard was duly issued with rifles and ammunition; then they assembled on the Market Square in front of the Midland Bank in the centre of town. Unbeknown to the Home Guard, previously Nurse had been called out to a patient. During the summer months mother always wore a white nurse's overall and on her return to Llanfair she parked the car in the garage some distance from our house. It was unfortunate that at the same time the Home Guard had been assembled on the Market Square – all feeling rather anxious and frightened. Suddenly, nurse appeared around the corner in her white smock. It was hard to say who was the most relieved: mother, for not having been shot at, or the nervous Home Guard! On another occasion the Home Guard had been called out on duty and issued with live ammunition. One member of the platoon accidentally discharged his rifle. Fortunately, no one was hit. This unexpected event did not engender a great deal of confidence in him by his fellow men.

The Home Guard were considered to be of great value in the event of an enemy invasion and to such ends they had to carry out exercises and military manoeuvres as well as regular practice on the firing range which was situated just outside Castle Caereinion village. One of the biggest exercises took place on a damp, drizzly day. Not only was the Home Guard involved but all the other local services as well, including the ARP (Air Raid Precautions), the Women's Voluntary Service, along with the local doctor and the nurse responsible for First Aid. The First Aid Post was based at the Institute and it was the role of our local GP, Dr Walter Milton Jones, to go around town tying labels to different people: for example, a person with 'a broken arm' or a 'head wound', and so on. These 'casualties' were then dispatched to the First Aid Post where mother was responsible for applying the correct treatment according to the attached label. To jolly the day along Dr Milton Jones had collared an elderly man not noted for his personal cleanliness who had not had a bath for some time. The doctor attached a 'broken toe' label to him. Mother then had to remove his boots and socks and dress the smelly feet accordingly. This was carried out with a great sense of fun.

Doctor [Walter] Milton Jones and Nurse were the two stalwarts of health care in Llanfair Caereinion and District. As 'Dr John', his son, states, in his foreword to this book, they worked together, as a team, for many years; and many people expressed their admiration and gratitude for all their good work. The Home Guard exercise did eventually turn out to be a bit of a farce. Some residents had been given blue armbands: these were defending Llanfair. Conversely, the ones with the white armbands were supposed to be attacking Llanfair. Each member of the Home Guard had been issued with a rifle and an attached string of paper caps. To 'shoot' one of the opposition one of these caps had to be activated. Unfortunately, the day was damp and no sound of gunfire was forthcoming – because the caps had become soggy. This enforced some of the defenders to take prisoners – an option that they had not contemplated beforehand.

It was the role of the Llanfair contingent of the Home Guard to defend Llanfair town when the attackers came from Welshpool and were not Welsh speaking. One of the Llanfair Home Guard had taken some 'prisoners' and did not know what to do with them. He enquired, in Welsh, to one of his superior officers,' Beth ydw i'n gallu wneud efo rhein?' ['What shall I do with these?'] His superior's reply was 'Saethu'r diawl' ['Shoot the devils]!

Among local youth and, indeed, the not so young, there were many pranksters. Unlike the pranks of today, the practical jokes of war-time Llanfair were not of a serious nature and no damage was caused. The long nights, with the enforced blackout lent itself to activities such as letting a dog into chapel when the service was in progress, sometimes with a tin can attached to its collar. In the surrounding country districts some pranksters hung five-bar gates from telegraph poles or used a cloth to cover up the masked headlights of a car. For a while this would leave the driver in turmoil. Most of these tricks were frivolous and harmless though it was noticeable that Nurse always enjoyed a free passage, so to speak. Yet, if she was ever in trouble with a puncture or had become stuck in the snow, those self-same pranksters were ever willing to help. Llanfair did have its full share of jokers. One was a Dick Goodwin (his photograph appears in Pryce 1991, p.158). At one time Dick was working for a local butcher in the town when he accidentally sliced off the top of his finger. Immediately he ran down to my mother who washed and dressed his fingers. When Nurse asked how the accident had happened he told her that he had been making sausages and was adamant that the tip of his finger had gone into a sausage. From that day on we never again had sausage in our house.

Throughout the war years public dances – we called them 'hops' – were held in Llanfair Institute. The dance band consisted of local musicians, ably led by Mr Thomas Oliver Roberts, a schoolteacher who was very versatile and could play almost any musical instrument. He was always conversant with all the tunes of the day. The band was known as the 'Llanfair Rhythm Fans Dance Band'. The entrance fee was one shilling (5p) and profits were denoted to various good war-time causes, such as the local 'Welcome Home Fund'.

For a short period two Land Army girls were billeted in our house. Hostels did exist for them at Welshpool but lodgings nearer the farms where they worked were much more convenient. It was at this time that my mother received an interesting letter from a 'Mr H. Jones' the father of one of these Land Army girls. Getting out his pen and ink Mr Jones writes to thank Nurse for the hospitality given to both girls in our house: ' . . . it did me good to hear how happy both are under you'! But he goes on to ask Nurse to provide the Land Army girls with some very personal advice:

> . . . Annie's mother never felt like talking on certain subjects . . . and also knowing you are a midwife, I would consider it a great favour if you would give Annie some information and advice on some for I realise how girls of this age need it specially when I see the low grade of morals around . . .

And further,

> . . . a word in time saves much pain later on, not only to Annie but to any girl. She in turn may inform some and who can tell where she may get to . . . perhaps [into] into your profession in another country for this war is certainly changing costoms [sic.] quick [sic.].

Although evidently not all that well educated, the writer, 'Mr H. Jones', as he signed himself, was showing concern for his young daughter and her lack of knowledge of worldly ways. His letter goes a long way in reflecting the challenges facing parents in wartime. Like so many others, Annie Jones, his daughter, had been sent out from home in a context where war was the dominating influence. Mr Jones recognized that self discipline would be important during these conditions. The original letter, reproduced in this book as Figure 27, is well worth reading, as much for its written style as for its wider significance. This letter is a poignant request by a father who was himself away from home through no fault of his own.

CHAPTER SIX

War-time Shortages

The threat of war came with a warning of forthcoming severe shortages of almost every commodity. With no idea how long the conflict was going to last, mother tackled the problems with her usual enthusiasm and skill. The outcome was that she was to become a hoarder for the rest of her life.

At the first hint of these shortages, one of her first purchases was a ton of coal. The coal was stored in an outhouse where the larger lumps were stacked to form a wall to retain the smaller broken lumps. We relied on a Triplex grate with a back boiler and an oven on one side for all our cooking and heating requirements.

We were very fortunate. Father, being a plumber, had installed a bathroom in our house, complete with a flush toilet and airing cupboard. Electric immersion heaters were not generally availbale then; so, the open fire was the only means of heating water. Consequently, a fire burned in the grate most of the time. Despite the availability of plenty of hot water, one bath a week for each member of our family was considered adequate. Probably this habit had derived from the days before our new grate had been installed when the old tin bath had to be filled with water carried in from an outside tap to which hot water, boiled in a large kettle on the open fire, was added.

In 1945, at the end of the war, a large amount of the coal,

originally purchased in 1939, was still left, unused. The coal was supplemented by the burning of logs. Timber was much needed for the war effort and, because of the serious risks to the lives of merchant seamen and their ships, importing it was not considered essential. So, locally, many trees were felled and, for the sum of twenty-five shillings (£1.25p – roughly £35 in today's money), the top of a felled tree could be purchased on site. During the war years, Mam bought a number of these. Because of my father's continuing poor health and the fact that my brother had been called up for service in the Fleet Air Arm, a branch of the Royal Navy, it was mother and I who went in search of firewood. Armed with a cross-cut saw and an axe, we spent hours sawing the larger boughs into six-foot lengths; and chopping and bagging the smaller branches and sticks for lighting our fire each morning. These were taken home in the boot of our car. The larger lengths were loaded on the lorry of a local haulier and stowed in an old building, later to be sawn into usable logs when required. When this operation had been completed, not a twig remained where the original tree had been felled. To supplement this source of fuel, every time Mam travelled around the country areas on her nursing duties, she never failed to come home without an old hedge stake or broken branches in the boot of her car. During the summer months, double British summertime was the order of the day and this enabled outdoor activities to continue until nearly midnight. This was to enable the farmers to gather their crops. There were no tractors and everything was done by horse. We would look forward to the time when the farmers brought wool by horse and cart to the central wool collection depôt just off the Market Square, next to the Black Lion Inn. When the empty carts were returning home we were allowed to sit on the rear of the cart for a fair distance and then we would walk back home. There was much of this sort of activity on Fair Days in Llanfair, especially the May Fair, usually held on the first Friday of that month, and known as 'Jones the Graig's Fair'. On these great events, numerous stalls lined the streets all the way up the street from the Methodist Chapel (Moriah) on the Market Square, to the lych-gate leading to the church from the High Street. Shire horses, in all their specially dressed harnesses and finery, would be run up and down the street. It was the time when farm labourers could seek new employment for the following year.

Another regular event during those wartime years was a need to purchase three or four rows of potatoes which would then be set by a farmer in one of his fields. As always, our family obtained their potato supply from Beudy Hir Farm, in mother's favourite area of Cefncoch. Invariably, because of its altitude the Beudyhir potato crop was a late one. However, a local farmer told me recently that Mam's choice of Cefncoch to purchase rows of potatoes made sound sense because the sandy soil lent itself to a good potato crop. Mother knew why she took this decision: after all, she was a farmer's daughter.

As with treetops, after school, mother and I, armed with a spade, fork and some empty sacks, would dig and bag the potatoes into the late evening. These were then brought home in the car. If, inadvertently, I was to slice a potato with the spade, or stuck a fork into a tuber whilst digging, I would be warned to be more careful, and I would be then given a lecture on how lucky we were to have any potatoes at all. As with the tree tops, when the harvesting of the potatoes had been completed not one remained – not even a small potato. The used ground was tidied up, and left for the farmer.

Our house, because it was a town house, did not have the benefit of a garden. A campaign by the war-time government, called 'Dig for Victory', was set in motion to encourage people to grow their own vegetables to supplement food shortages. Any small areas of waste land within the town could be used for this purpose. Llanfair's response to the campaign was to cultivate a large expanse of waste ground around the town's tennis courts – today used as a car park and play area for children. This land was divided into a number of small plots and allocated to townspeople. Hitherto, untried gardeners became experts in their own right and the rivalry was keen. One of the approaches to these allotments was through what is today the former builder's yard of Morgan Brothers at the bottom of Bridge Street. During the 1940s, four or five inhabited cottages were in this yard and the through path was regarded as a public right of way. It is interesting to note that in the early days of the war a communal air raid shelter was being dug in the field at the end of the yard. This consisted of a large deep trench dug into the sloping ground. The intention was to cover this over to provide a safe shelter should bombs fall, but the project was never completed.

Further down the same field there was a large ladder-type stile which gave access to the war-time garden allotments and to the bowling green. Near this stile was a large pipe running down to the river (Afon Banw). By this means water could be pumped up for use on the town's bowling green.

A long-term resident of Llanfair town once related the following amusing story to me. Most of the local youth were in the habit of catching trout and salmon in the river using the method known locally as 'maggling'. This entailed the attaching of two strands of the wire used for making rabbit snares in a noose on the end of a stick, which was then used for snaring fish in the river. One of the older boys, an ardent poacher, who later became a doctor, once informed some youngsters that if they wished to catch fish they should set snares on the bowling green and catch the fish as they came up the pipe! The bowling green keeper could never understand why rabbit snares were placed on the green.

When the town's bowling green was constructed in the early 1930s, a considerable depth of clinkers, collected from the Llanfair Railway, were laid down to provide good drainage. Turfs from Borth Bog, near Aberystwyth, were then laid to provide a good-quality smooth surface. But, with the outbreak of war, bowling matches ceased, and, unfortunately, someone spread farm manure on the green. In consequence, fed by the rich nutrients, the formerly well-kept short grass grew rapidly and the green was destroyed. Following the end of the war, the local schools used the green as grass tennis courts and it was not until 1969 that the old bowling green was finally restored to provide the excellent facilities that we have today.

Another of mother's efforts to ensure that we did not go hungry was the purchase of a few chickens to provide a ready supply of fresh eggs. These were kept on a sloping piece of ground, with a fruit orchard, directly in front of what is today the High School. Making her own bread was another of mother's activities. She continued doing this until well after the end of hostilities: indeed, probably she was the last person in Llanfair town to make her own bread on a regular basis. The making of the bread was a well-organized operation. The dough was kneaded and prepared in an old-fashion bathtub made of tin. When ready, a cloth was put over the dough and it was left in front of the fire to rise – often overnight. The risen dough was then cut up and put on trays, usually the upturned lids of large tins. These were then taken to one of the town's bake houses to be baked where a small fee was charged for this service. Bread was always baked on a Tuesday morning, so mother had to be up very early to prepare the dough, and she had to make sufficient to last the week. The bread, when fresh, was wonderful but by the next Tuesday, although still edible, it had become dry and hard to eat.

Of course nothing was ever wasted. The flour, purchased in white linen sacks, was then stored in a dust bin specially bought for this purpose and used for nothing else. Then the stitching on the sacks was unravelled, the sack was washed and was used eventually as clean white linen for the table. The name of the flour merchant, 'A & A Peate, Oswestry', was stamped on the sacks but after a few washes this soon disappeared. Anyone who can remember these sacks will agree that they were made of the finest quality linen.

Washing day, usually on a Monday, was a torrid affair. A fire was lit under an old boiler in the outside washhouse – and I recall vividly that very little of its smoke actually went up the chimney! After a good boiling and much rubbing on the washing board, the whites would be rinsed in water in which a block of 'Reckitts Blue' had been placed. This made the whites look whiter. After that, the clothes would have to be passed between wooden rollers in a cast-iron mangle. All the water used on washing day had to be carried in buckets and disposed of by hand. Until the mains electricity arrived in Llanfair the ironing had to be done by heating old block irons (flat irons) on the fire.

Jam making was another activity encouraged by the government and this, too, was taken up with great enthusiasm by Mam. She always made damson jam because the fruit was plentiful and cheap. To encourage jam making at home the government authorized an extra sugar allowance. Because it had to be shipped from abroad, and because more vital goods were required for the war effort, sugar was in extremely short supply. In consequence, the normal allotted weekly ration per person was a very meagre amount. Needless to say, the extra sugar was not all used for jam making! Both mother and I had stopped taking sugar in our tea when food rationing began. When rationing finished, I succumbed, but mother never afterwards returned to the taking of sugar in her tea. We also picked whinberries (*llus duon bach* in Welsh) which still grow in short bushy undergrowth on the moorlands beyond Cefncoch. This was a chore that I hated. But to taste those delicious tarts made out of them made it all worthwhile – although whinberries do leave the tongue and gums with a strong tinge of bluish purple.

Farmers were always very generous to mother and often she received gifts of fresh eggs, home-made butter as well as the occasional bottle of buttermilk. My father loved buttermilk, especially on new potatoes, but I was never keen on its flavour.

Mother was very partial to hard-boiled fresh eggs. Once on her visit to a small farmer whose wife had just given birth to her first child, as the confinement was over by breakfast time, the father gave mother a hard-boiled egg for breakfast. This same family eventually had nine children and after every confinement mother was treated to a hard-boiled egg!

Because refrigerators were not in general use, during the 1940s it was extremely difficult to preserve some foods. Butter was always a problem and could not be kept long before it became rancid. Eggs, on the other hand, were put in a large earthenware pot and preserved in a gelatine mixture. Most small farmers reared, killed and salted their own pigs; and the flitches of bacon and ham were hung in the house for their own use. There were restrictive regulations on the number of pigs that could be slaughtered privately but in the country districts, these rules and regulations were generally flouted. On two or three occasions during the war years mother purchased half a pig to supplement our meat rations. The side of bacon and leg of ham was hung in the attic at home and slices were cut off, as and when required. The spare ribs from a farm-killed pig are something we shall never taste the likes of again. From other parts of the carcass brawn was made. This, too, was a very tasty supper dish. From the fat, rough bars of soap were made and this home-made soap was used to do the weekly clothes wash – again supplementing a rationed product. One wonders today about the warnings that eating too much animal fat can lead to all manner of health problems. But back in the past, the home-cured sides of bacon contained only a mere couple of thin streaks of lean meat running through them, and, in consequence, the breakfast plate would be swimming in fat.

As a young boy, I recall spending a holiday on the farm of my grandparents. Like all farmers in those days, they killed their own pigs and when the fried ham had been eaten, the bottom of the plate would be awash with fat. With relish, this was then mopped up with lumps of unbuttered bread. Bread and dripping was another firm favourite. After roasting the meat, the dried fat in the bottom of the dish was spread on bread. This was very tasty. Both my grandparents lived to a ripe old age, my grandmother well into her nineties – so much for fat-free eating! The authorities frowned on the purchasing of extra meat on the black market. A local butcher was once prosecuted for supplying more than the allotted rations of meat and he was required to appear before local magistrates. However, my parents' consciences were eased a great deal on that winter night when they went to collect half a pig from a local farmer: when they drove into the farmyard, the local police sergeant was seen in their headlight beams carrying half of a pig to his car!

Every Christmas mother purchased half a dozen or so geese, still in their feathers, from a local farmer. These were plucked and prepared at home, a very tiresome and difficult chore indeed. Then the geese were 'dressed' and distributed to her sisters and other close relatives as a Christmas gift. Often, I was coerced into helping mother pluck these geese. We did this task in a small room with the doors and windows firmly closed. There would be feathers and down everywhere. The whole operation was very sore on the thumb and after they had been plucked a piece of newspaper was lit and held underneath the bird to singe away the feather down. An old neighbour recalls the time when mother was doing the plucking by herself when she had an urgent nursing call out. Our friendly neighbour and her husband finished the plucking.

As mentioned earlier, two of Mam's sisters lived in the suburbs of Manchester – one a teacher, the other a health visitor. During the war years city dwellers were far more disadvantaged than we were and they had difficulties in supplementing their meagre food rations. Both my maternal aunts owned cars, which, because of the acute petrol shortages, were stored on blocks in their garages for the duration of the war. So, for them, return trips back to Wales to obtain fresh food supplies was exceedingly difficult. Only people providing vital services for their local communities were allowed a petrol ration; and, being a nurse in a rural district, mother had a reasonable amount of petrol available for her use. On at least two occasions, accompanied by myself, mother would load up our Austin Eight with any available foodstuff that she could lay her hands on – potatoes, vegetables, meat and butter – and then she would drive up to Chadderton (on the other side of Manchester) to give the much-appreciated food to her sisters and their families.

As well as her nursing duties, because of my father's illness, Mam continued to run the family's painting, decorating and glazing business as well as our small retail shop. Mam's heavy workload meant that a maid had to be employed to run the house and answer the telephone. In this way mother could then concentrate on her nursing duties and manage the family business.

CHAPTER SEVEN

The Family Business in War-time

Throughout the 1940s two or three painters were employed in our family painting and decorating business. Even though most of the able bodied men had been called up for active service in one of the armed forces, schools and other public buildings had to be maintained and with her usual enthusiasm mother took up the reins of the business. Her responsibilities included preparing estimates as to the costs for specific jobs, ordering materials, and undertaking the necessary clerical and administrative work. Her duties involved working out and paying the men's wages and the sending out of the monthly accounts to our many customers. In fact Mam did everything except, of course, the actual work of painting.

As with every other basic commodity, paint, too, was very difficult to obtain in wartime. It was supplied in five gallon (25 litres) drums which were not very convenient for the much smaller quantities that were sold in our shop. This problem was overcome by pouring the paint into one pound (in weight) jam jars. The top was then covered with brown paper, tied with string and the details of the contents were written out on the brown paper.

As glaziers, we also sold window glass over the counter in our shop. The putty for fixing the glass into window frames also came in large kegs: so, the correct amount for each individual glass pane had to be weighed out. The glass arrived in large wooden crates at Llanfair Light Railway station, along with many other goods. A member of the station staff brought these into the town on a hand truck and the empty crates were collected by the same means.

People called at the shop to order a pane of glass that we would then have to cut to size. If our customers did not have the means of measuring the size of glass required they would produce a small straight stick taken from a hedgerow and cut a notch on it to signify the width required and the length of the stick would be the length of the glass pane required. There were many odd tasks, which, as painters and decorators, we were asked to carry out – many of them not expected of tradesmen today. For example, often we were called upon to paint the name of a deceased person, their age and date of death on a brass plate that was fixed on their coffin. Another regular request was for lead weights for fitting on the horns of cattle. These weights were fashioned out of pieces of lead piping. I think they helped to control the direction in which the horns grew. During the earlier years of our family business one of the glaziers would carry a keg of putty, setsquare and glass cutter on his bicycle. Equipped with a stout webbing bag slung over his shoulder, which contained sheets of glass and was known as 'a devil', the glazier went on his bicycle into outlying areas to replace any broken window panes.

Another oddity of those far-off days was the treatment that we applied for dealing with the stains that showed through in a newly distempered ceilings. Nicotine stains, in particularly, can be a problem on the ceilings of pub bars. So, a sealer, to prevent the stains showing through, was put on before distempering. First, the ceiling was washed down and then a coat of *biswel* (collected from a farm mixen) was applied. This normally solved the problem. *Biswel* is the Welsh name we use for that wet substance that oozes out from a heap of farmyard manure! Special wallpaper paste was not readily available, so ordinary household flour was used. This had to be mixed with boiling water but it was very difficult to do this without lumps forming in the mixture. Nevertheless, in retrospect it seems that its adhesive qualities were far superior to many brand-named wallpaper pastes available today. Another skill used by painters and decorators was that of 'graining' different types of surface. Doors, especially chapel doors, were figured and brush-grained to imitate mahogany, oak or quartered oak. Probably today the cost for this type of finish would be very high.

Mother usually delivered many of the goods sold in our shop as she went on her rounds as the district nurse – a service no longer provided by shopkeepers for reasons of cost, even in a small town like Llanfair. Very often a local small shopkeeper would purchase some paint, wallpaper and other decorating materials from our shop. This would be delivered by mother who would then purchase goods of approximately the same value from the shop keeper. Little or no money changed hands and everyone was satisfied. This neighbourly act helped to create a friendly atmosphere among local shopkeepers. What a lovely way to do business! Sometimes, as when customers could not afford to pay the full amount for the purchased goods immediately, a weekly sum, paid as an instalment, would be acceptable. This could be as little as sixpence (6d – 2.5p in decimal currency) per week and there was no extra charge for the granting of extended credit. On one occasion one of our employees wanted to buy a property costing £900 (the equivalent of about £24,974 in today's value). Mother lent him the purchase price and deducted a set amount from his wages every week. Again, no interest was ever charged. When the wages of skilled craftsmen in the painting and decorating trades had reached between £8 and £10 per week (the equivalent of between £222 and £278 today), according to our account books our employees were getting substantially less – though the full amount was made up in ready cash. Apart from convenience to the employee, the other reason for this was that they paid little or no tax. Father warned my mother that if ever she was caught it was she who would be sent to prison for this apparent breach of the law. But clearly, even the business side of Mam's life was geared to thought for others.

All mother's family were ardent chapel goers and our chapel meant a great deal to Mam throughout her life. She often recalled an incident from her own childhood when, along with other children, she was in Sunday school at Y Fan, near Llanidloes, where she had been brought up. A motorcycle was heard approaching and all the children dashed out of the chapel to see this wonderful machine! Mother also told us of other memories from her childhood days. When an accident occurred at the nearby lead mines, the siren was sounded and the injured man would be brought down on a railway truck to Van Terrace, in the hamlet of Y Fan, where many of the miners lived. On one occasion, the siren had sounded and the small train carrying the injured men stopped opposite the terrace of houses. The wife of one of the injured men asked him if he was dead. When he replied that he wasn't, the wife stated that he was such a big liar that she didn't believe him!

My grandmother regularly attended Manledd Chapel at Y Fan all her life. When she was in her late 80s, despite her failing eyesight, she gave an extended reading to the congregation from the Bible. Someone noticed that she held the Bible upside down – evidence that she was reciting the passage from memory. Grandmother was honoured when she was awarded the famous Gee Medal in recognition of her attendances at Sunday school for over eighty years.

Not long after my mother had started nursing duties in Llanfair, grandmother decided to pay her a visit. She asked Nurse if she was still attending chapel. Nurse replied that she was too busy but that she regularly paid her membership subscription and otherwise supported the chapel financially. Her mother retorted by informing Nurse that she could not buy her way into heaven! If this had any affect on Nurse it is difficult to say but she did attend Bethesda, the Wesleyan Chapel in Llanfair, at every opportunity. If she was late returning from her nursing duties she would slip into a rear pew of the chapel. If she was expecting a call she would sit in the pew nearest the door so that she could be summoned out without disturbing the service.

For many years Mam was a trustee of Bethesda chapel and after her death a reading light was provided for the lectern in her memory, together with a small memorial plaque bearing her name. It is sad to record that after not having been used for some years, the Bethesda Chapel was demolished in 1983 (see Pryce, 1991, p.122, 206, 208). As far I am aware there is still a small box of medical equipment in the doctors' clinic at Caereinion Health Centre with a brass plaque in memory of Nurse.

A district nurse and midwife during the war years had to cope with numerous problems of rationing under war-time restrictions. Only essential services were allowed a petrol ration and it was compulsory to have car headlights fitted with diffusing masks. These had three or four narrow slits in them to reduce the light, which, it was thought, might be spotted by enemy aircraft. To make matters more difficult, apart from homes in Llanfair town, which were lighted by electricity, most people relied on candles, paraffin lamps and lanterns for lighting purposes. It was not until 1950, long after the war had ended, that the Banw valley was connected to the national electricity grid. This was hastened by the fact that the town's own electricity generating station had been destroyed by fire that year. Luckily, the Merseyside and North Wales Electricity Board were already in the process of erecting supply lines between Welshpool and Llanfair (see Pryce, 1991, pp 160-61). Under the difficult conditions of war time not only did mother carry out all her nursing duties – the distribution of National Dried Milk, etc. and the supply and fitting of gas masks to infants and young children – but, also, she continued to run the painting business.

War-time blackout regulations had to be adhered to strictly. Not even a chink of light could be seen from the houses and, of course, all street lighting in the town had been dismantled. Any light seen by German bombers on their way to bomb the prime target, Liverpool and its docks, would be an invitation for bombs to be dropped on Llanfair town. Some enemy bombs were dropped locally. The nearest, I recall, fell in a field close to Cyfronydd Hall. No one was injured although a few sheep were killed and some panes of glass in the big house itself were shattered by the blast. The Observation Post situated on Cae Boncyn in the Wynnstay Fields would have had advanced warnings of approaching aircraft. Whereas larger towns and cities had loud sirens to warn of the approach of enemy aircraft, smaller towns like Llanfair relied on Air Raid Wardens who would walk around the town, blowing a whistle and shouting 'Put that light out'. But there were many other precautions against air raids. Schools and public buildings had strips of tape or a type of lace net stuck to the inside of window panes so that should a bomb be dropped in the vicinity the glass would not splinter and fly around – thus incidental injuries could be avoided. An essential need for the midwife delivering a baby was a constant supply of hot water. In most homes the only way of heating water was by a kettle on an open fire. Some larger farmhouses had an old-fashioned, black-leaded grate with a cooking oven on one side and a water boiler on the other with a lift-up lid. The hot water was taken out in a small jug or noggin. Either way, the water took a long time to heat.

When I was a pupil at the Council (formerly the Board) School in Mount Road, now used as our Ysgol Feithrin, we regularly went through exercises as to what to do in the event of a real air raid. We were told to run up the nearby little brook, known as Nant y Bwt, and hide under the trees! This would not have afforded us much protection against shrapnel from a bomb. But, to us youngsters it was great fun! A relic of wartime Llanfair can still be seen behind Crown House in High Street.

This is a round concrete block approximately 2¹/₂ feet high with a girth of 6 feet. Several of the concrete defence blocks still remain in the yard behind the former Morgan Brothers' stores where they are now used as a part of a retaining wall. In the event of the enemy approaching the town these blocks were to be placed across the road in strategic positions to hold up the military vehicles (Figure 13). In the same place a stout wire rope was to be fixed also across the road to prevent any enemy motorcyclists passing. There were several sites for these barricades including those on the bridge on the Melin-y-ddôl road near the entrance to the Deri Woods and another in Llanfair town on the bridge at the bottom of Bridge Street. The wire was to be set about three feet above the road surface and was attached to steel rings embedded in the bridge walls.

Another relic of wartime Llanfair can be seen in the field on the Llanfair side of Heniarth Farm. This is the sole Nissen hut still remaining of the three that accommodated a fully manned searchlight battery during World War II (Figure 17). During the war years the family living at the nearby Heniarth Mill were well known poultry producers. It was said that, prior to going home on leave, the soldiers would catch a chicken and take it home to be enjoyed as an extra treat for their meagrely-rationed families. One night it was discovered that someone had stolen the wall clock from the Llanfair Railway station: in those days this act was regarded as 'a terrible crime'. The culprits were apprehended and they turned out to be the soldiers manning the searchlight battery. Our Special Constables, part-time police officers, were credited with having solved this major crime. These war-time police officers were recruited from men too old to join the armed forces. Nevertheless, they took their role very seriously, even though most of the 'crimes' solved concerned the riding of bicycles without any lights! The 'Specials' included Mr Millington, haulier, who lived at Broncafnant (for some reason, better known locally as 'The College'); Mr Davies, the grocer, whose shop was next to the National Provincial Bank (now the

NatWest Bank) in High Street; Mr I.O. Evans, painter, and Mr W.J. Watkin, later our local registrar for births, marriages and deaths.

Mr Millington, mentioned above, was the owner of a small lorry that he hired out for light haulage. As one of the largest painting and decorating firms in Montgomeryshire, during the summer holiday period, our family firm would normally have the contract to paint and decorate five or six schools, both inside and outside, for the Montgomeryshire Education Authority. The cost of materials constituted the largest sum, by far, in the quoted price. The lack of transport meant that the painters would have to sleep in those schools a good distance away from Llanfair town. Imagine the scene on a Monday morning. Each painter was responsible for bringing his own food, camp bed and bedclothes. There had to be sufficient food to last a whole working week. All our personal equipment, together with all the paint, materials, ladders and planks etc., had to be loaded on Mr Millington's lorry. Since portable transistor radios did not exist, entertainment of any sort was unavailable – except, of course, at the local pub.

Many of the small schools on which we worked were in very remote districts with no local inns or public houses. So, we had to make our own entertainment in the long evenings. The following is an account of how we entertained ourselves at Brooks School, near Berriew, where we worked as painters. The school yard was enclosed with yards and yards of iron railings, all of which had to be stripped and painted – a tedious job. Every night, before going to sleep, invariably the subject of conversation amongst the working men was that of ghosts – no doubt petrifying to some of the younger painters. One moonlight night, except my father, all the men had gone out for a long walk prior to turning in. Using a painter's white smock and some string Dad rigged an 'apparition' over the beams above his camp bed. When the other painters returned, as usual they were talking about ghosts. As they arrived, Dad pulled the string and the white 'apparition' rose in the moonlight on the other side of the glass partition. The reaction was catastrophic. One of the younger painters threw his boots at the 'ghost' and ran off down the road in horror shouting 'To hell with Brooks and the railings'. It took a great deal of persuasion to convince him to return.

On another occasion a very 'correct' gentleman painter, who had recently joined our family firm, brought with him a new-fangled, air-filled mattress on which to sleep but the air had to be pumped in before he left home on the Monday morning. Unfortunately, this new mattress sprang a leak in the early hours of the morning and the workman did not make himself very popular by waking all the other painters and asking every one of us if we had a pump!

After the end of the war, transport problems eased and it was no longer necessary for the workers to sleep on camp beds in the schools where they were working. Nevertheless, usually it was cheaper for us to take lodgings locally rather than travel to work from Llanfair every day. We had the contract for glazing and painting the newly-built High School at Machynlleth. This meant that we had to lodge in Machynlleth town from Monday night until noon on Saturday. Because food was still rationed, each painter was responsible for taking sufficient food for the week; and the landlady then prepared meals for him from these supplies. Some of the painters, who were lodging with two elderly ladies, were expected to stand around the piano and sing hymns after they had returned back to their lodgings after the pubs had closed (at 9.30pm those days). But as the costs of daily travel fell, in later years we began to travel daily from Llanfair to work in places as far afield as Aberystwyth.

CHAPTER EIGHT

Our Home in Bridge Street
and the Llanfair Floods

Since the middle of the nineteenth century, our family have lived and owned trade premises in Bridge Street in Llanfair Caereinion town. Consequently, over many years, the regular flooding of Bridge Street was a cause of great concern. The earliest known print of Llanfair, derived from a drawing by George Samuel, is dated c.1790. This shows two streams, Nant y Bwt and Nant Cafnant, converging in front of the old market hall. The merged waters then flowed down the west side of Bridge Street into Afon Banw (see Pryce 1991, pp 32 and 47). At some later date, these streams were placed underground in culverts. The outlet for the water is still in use and can be seen by looking over the side of Llanfair bridge. It emerges into Afon Banw directly from under Bridge House. Blockages within these underground culverts could cause severe flooding in Bridge Street and this was a frequent occurrence until a few years back. J.W. Ellis, the photographer, who lived in Bridge Street, recorded the floods in 1908 and again in 1910 (see Pryce, 1991, pp. 53, 78). In 1934/35 the local council decided to widen and extend the culverts in Bridge Street. Figure 15, which shows the work in progress, is a photograph taken from the roof of the present-day HSBC Bank (formerly the Midland Bank) on the Market Square. This shows the newly dug-out culverts passing down through Bridge Street. On the right can be seen Rathbone House, our family home, and the front of our shop. The premises was named after the collection of wall-papers displayed in a pattern book called 'The Rathbone Collection'.

Next door, across the gap that is the entrance to a row of old cottages known as Duck Street, stood Paris House. This was the shop and home of David Astley, master tailor. In the buildings at the rear was the tailor's workshop, where his skilled employees cut cloth and made garments, including high quality suits for men. The large windows, necessary for good natural lighting conditions so that the tailors could see their fine work, still exist. Duck Street was a narrow urban lane than runs along the rear of all the houses and shops fronting on to Bridge Street: from the Methodist House (Maldwyn House) to Jubilee House, the premises of the late Empson Davies and his wife, with their separate hair-dressing 'salons' for women and men. Here, men could be shaved – a service provided by Empson, using the old cut-hroat wet razors. Jubilee House was named such because the business was started in 1935, the year of the Royal Jubilee. Four or five of these old cottages backed directly onto the town's churchyard and burial ground.

The boy shown standing on the walkway across the open culvert in Figure 16 is my brother John. The man nearby is Mr Harry Phillips, a veteran of the First World War. Further up the street can be seen Jane Roderick (left centre in Figure 16). The mother of Mr Phillips, Jane, lived in one of the small cottages in Duck Street that backed on the graveyard. Unfortunately, in the late 1940s her cottage went on fire and she was burned to death. But this was not the only tragedy for this old Llanfair family. Harry's son, George Phillips, volunteered for the army when, in fact, he was only 16 years old – telling the enrolling officer that he had reached his 17th birthday. He was killed on active service in France and his name can be seen on the parish war memorial in High Street.

But, as it turned out, the enlarged culverts beneath Bridge

Street were not all that effective in alleviating flooding in the town and flooding still continued to occur. I recall that the flood of 1951 was one of the most severe in the damage it caused. As Nant y Bwt and Nant Cafnant swelled, from inside the houses along the west side of Bridge Street we heard the sounds of stones as they rumbled down the culverts under the force of the water.

But most memorable was the severe flash flood that caused something akin to a tidal wave that rushed down Bridge Street on Wednesday September 3 in 1958. Our shop and the sitting room on the ground floor of our home were flooded to a depth approaching three feet. The door to our shop and many small tins of paint in stock were swept away in the flood. When the waters subsided, everywhere was left covered by a layer of muddy slime. The shops and houses on the east side of Bridge Street, opposite our own shop and home, fared even worse. Many had cellars where their retail stock and domestic goods had been stored. Everything was ruined.

Figure 12 is from a photograph taken after the main floodwaters had receded. The small crowd standing on the Market Square in front of the then Midland Bank (Figure 12, again, mid distance, right) were all local people, people known to me. They had hired a bus to take them to see the football team, Wolverhampton Wanderers, playing at home. Because of the severe flood these enthusiastic soccer fans never made it to the match. The scene recorded in Figure 18 gives us some idea as to the ferocity of the flood. The three-ton lorry shown in this photograph had been parked outside the shop of William Jones & Sons, grocers (Old Bank House) at the top of Bridge Street where the driver had been delivering stock for the shop. The force of the floodwater was such that the lorry was swept down Bridge Street, crashing in the process. As can be seen from Figures 19 and 20, the flood caused a great deal of damage to the shop and showrooms owned by Morgan Brothers, iron mongers and general merchants. The Llanfair Fire Brigade was called out to pump water from the cellars. In addition, many volunteers came to help in clearing up after the flood. Such a disaster generates the best spirit of co-operation and help in people.

There are two positive aspects that we need to record about this particular flood and the damage it caused. The first is the fact that this was essentially a flash flood that occurred suddenly at 4.30pm on that hot Wednesday afternoon in September 1958, following several days of unsettled weather with rumbles of thunder. If it had happened earlier that afternoon, the children would have been walking up Bridge Street after school had ended. The potential consequences do not bear thinking about. Secondly, this catastrophe moved the local District Council to take remedial action by directing Nant Cafnant away from Nant y Bwt. This work was eventually completed in 1966. The underground section starts from the end of the town's car park in Watergate Street, and then passes beneath the church yard to a new outflow into Afon Banw. This scheme seems to have solved Llanfair's long-time flooding problems. In February 1999 Afon Banw reached its highest flood levels for over 40 years (Figures 21 and 22). But, despite periods of heavy prolonged rainfall, no flooding has occurred again in Llanfair town.

In many respects the floods of September 1958 caused more damage in Bridge Street than it would have done today – simply because of the closure of so many long-established retail businesses. In 1958 the shops and businesses in Llanfair's Bridge Street still served a very large area and almost any everyday need could be purchased in its shops (Figure 23). Today, only three premises are still used for business purposes: the dentist's surgery in Old Bank House, the offices of the National Farmer's Union in Victoria House and the former shop and hardware stores under the name Morgan Bros (Brothers), which was the only business to survive after the severe flooding in 1958 (now closed).

CHAPTER NINE

Public Acknowledgement for Nurse

On Tuesday January 21 1958, Nurse contributed to the radio programme, Deupen y Daith ('Both Ends of a Journey'), broadcasted on the BBC Welsh Home Service. The whole programme was in Welsh, mother's first language. The two-fold themes focused on a young Nurse, Miss Mair Owen, from Caernarfon, then just starting out on her career, and mother, who, by this date, had been working in the nursing profession for over forty years. Together, they discussed the many changes that had taken place in the responsibilities and the work of a district nurse and midwife in rural Wales. The radio presenter was the Reverend Islwyn Ffowc Elis, the widely known novelist and public figure, who had been the minister of Moriah, the Calvinistic Methodist Chapel in Llanfair. Islwyn Ffowc Elis had lived in the town for a number of years before moving to Anglesey. He left the ministry to become a free-lance writer and BBC producer and, eventually, a full-time college lecturer and university academic. So, in a very real sense the presenter had a close knowledge of life in Llanfair, which is reflected in some of his writings; and he was fully aware of the various active roles played by my mother in the local community.

In introducing the programme The Radio Times stated:

6.40 DEUPEN Y DAITH
Bob Nos Fawrth, daw i'r stiwdio ddau neu ddwy sydd yn yr un

alwedigaeth. Mae un yn nyddiau cynnar ei yrfa a'r llall o gwmpas oed ymneilltuo, a chânt gyfle i gymharu eu gwaith ddoe a heddiw. Heno, cawn glywed dwy Nyrs Ardal: Hannah Mills Evans a Mair Owen.

[Every Tuesday night two people of the same calling come into the studio. One is setting out on her career and the other is nearing completion and [in this programme] they are given the opportunity to compare their work yesterday and today. Tonight, we shall hear from two District Nurses, Hannah Mills Evans and Mair Owen.]

The following is a transcript of the radio interview, translated into English:

Islwyn Ffowc Ellis (IFE):
How many years have you been a nurse in Montgomeryshire?

Nurse Mills Evans (Nurse):
Next year, 1959, will be my fortieth year. I am the longest serving district nurse in the county and there are twenty two of us all together. During those forty years I have helped to deliver over 1,600 babies. [Nurse delivered more than 1,700 babies during her career.]

IFE:
You have seen many changes during your professional career. What has changed most during your time as a nurse in a rural area?

Nurse:
Firstly, perhaps, the salary. When I started the pay was £2 per week and, at that time, this amount was considered to be the largest salary in the county for a nurse. Most of the nurses did not get more than £78 per annum. The only additional payment was £2 5s [£2.25] for the upkeep of a bicycle. There was also a sum of £5 per annum to provide a uniform. I realised that a bicycle was not really practical to cover such a large hilly area. So, in 1923 I bought myself a motorcycle. In all, I have had seven motorbikes and made good use of them. In 1935 I bought a car. During my work as a nurse I have had ten cars, each one travelling over 1,200 miles every year.

IFE:
What is the size of the district under your care?

Nurse:
About 140 square miles of difficult, high and mountainous country.

IFE:
Well then, how do you manage to travel around your district in bad weather?

Nurse:

I have never yet failed to get to a case. In snow I have had to go on horseback and, more recently, by tractor. If the journey wasn't far, I would walk through the snow. The most peculiar journey I recall was during the hard winter of 1947 when there were snowdrifts over seven feet high in places. I was wanted on an urgent case and a friend informed me that a caterpillar tractor was taking fodder to starving, snow-bound sheep in that district. They put a ladder up against the load of hay and I got on top of the load, a friend accompanied me for support because the load was swaying. I finished my case and returned, safe and sound, with the same tractor.

IFE:

What other changes have you seen during your years of nursing?

Nurse:

When I started nursing in Montgomeryshire I was working for the County Nursing Association of which the Llanfair Caereinion District Nursing Association was a part.

The Associations relied on subscriptions and donations as well as the small fee that was charged to patients for the nursing care received. These fees were charged in ratio to the income of the patient. For example, old age pensioners were treated free; a labourer had only to pay two shillings [10p] per annum; small farmers three shillings [15p] per annum; and bigger farmers and trades people four shillings [20p] per annum. For the labourer, a midwifery case was charged at two shillings and six pence [13p], small farmers fifteen shillings [75p] and big farmers and business people £1. It was the nurse's duty to collect these midwifery fees but I never experienced difficulty in collecting them and they were always paid up with thanks. If a doctor was required on a midwifery case, and the family could not afford to pay, the County Council would cover the cost. Things are much different now after changing to the National Health Service in 1948. Every case can now have a nurse and a doctor, if required; and receive the best attention, free. I think the Health Service is a great advantage and help – especially to the poorer people. A doctor can be summoned at very short notice and the patient removed to hospital if necessary.

We also have, within thirty miles of us, a mobile emergency squad. One of the greatest aids to obtaining speedy help for the seriously ill is the telephone. There used to be only one in every village but now there are many public kiosks as well as private phones.

IFE:

Have you ever had a frightening experience while travelling about your district at night?

Nurse:

The most frightening experience I have had was while returning home from a call at 2am in the early hours of a summer morning, wearing a white nursing overall. As I turned the corner into Llanfair Caereinion, the Home Guard had been alerted for duty and was paraded on the street, ready for action. My approach at that hour had taken them by surprise. When I saw them getting their guns ready I was really frightened until I heard a familiar voice say 'It's only the Nurse, boys'!

When I went into my house I told my husband about the incident. His only reply was 'I bet they were probably more frightened than you'.

Another time out on duty in the early hours I heard aeroplanes flying low. I got out of the car to see them and to my horror one of the planes crashed in flames, about two fields away from where I was standing. I ran towards the aeroplane in the hope of saving life but I could not get near enough because of the exploding ammunition. I went back to the car and straightaway notified the village police. Unfortunately, the crew had been killed outright.

Another interesting experience occurred during the early part of my nursing service attending to a gypsy confinement. They would never book a case and when they did fetch me you could be sure that the baby would have been born before I had arrived. I think this was in case the family might be removed to the workhouse. They never gave me a great welcome and would much prefer if I did not visit them again. But it was my duty to visit them daily for ten days, which I did. The only reason they called me was because I would notify the authorities of the birth. They were fully aware that, if this was not done, proceedings would be taken against them. These gypsies usually lived in pegged tents, with a fire in the middle of the tent, and a hole at the top to let out the smoke. My eyes were continually watering and burning because of the smoke – though it didn't appear to affect them.

The babies were born on hay without bedclothes and the usual comforts. Usually the parents had prepared little in the way of clothes and equipment for the new baby. I remember once making a fifteen mile journey on such a case. On the third morning after the birth of the child, the tent and the family had gone, including the mother and baby. The farmer, who lived nearby, did not know where they had gone but apparently they had left soon after my second visit.

IFE:
What does your work consist of mainly?

Nurse:
General nursing and midwifery. I also attend eight schools monthly to examine the children's health and cleanliness. When the County Medical

Officer visits these schools for the medical inspection, I attend to help the doctor. Also I do health visiting and distribute welfare foods such as National Dried Milk, Orange Juice and Cod Liver Oil.

IFE:
What do you remember most in your nursing experience?

Nurse:
The kindness of the people of Llanfair Caereinion and the surrounding area for over forty years. In all aspects they have showed nothing but kindness, summer and winter, night and day. In every home I enter I always received a warm welcome. I would like to take this opportunity to thank them all, sincerely, for their help and kindness towards me throughout the time I have worked amongst them.

[End of the radio interview.]

Included in the script for the radio interview were two further questions that were to be asked if time allowed. As it turned out, these questions and Nurse's answers were not included in the broadcast. However, they are of considerable interest:

IFE:
How did you treat a case of pneumonia?

Nurse:
Well, if someone has pneumonia they are very ill indeed and a cause of great concern. Twice a day I have to apply a linseed poultice to the patient, who has to be washed with lukewarm water every four hours and kept under regular observance, night and day, for nine days. Hopefully, the illness would improve and the patient would feel better.

IFE:
What do you think of your work?

Nurse:
I had no thoughts of doing anything else. To me it has always been very pleasurable work from which I have derived a great deal of satisfaction from the day I started. The work has been full of surprises but I have never overcome the wonder and thankfulness of seeing a new baby coming into the world.

It was my brother who had driven Nurse up to Bangor on that January day for the radio broadcast. After the broadcast was over, my mother, brother and the other nurse were invited to the

119

home of the Revd. Islwyn Ffowc Elis for supper. It was a dreadful night and it was snowing heavily. The Reverend Ffowc Elis begged mother to stay overnight because it was not fit to travel. Nurse told him that a lady had booked her services for a confinement the following day, and that she couldn't possibly stay. They arrived back in Llanfair at 2am. At 2.30am mother was called out to deliver the baby.

The mention of the use of a poultice in one of the standby answers for the radio programme brings back unpleasant memories. I can recall numerous people coming to our house, suffering from boils, usually on the back of the neck. In fact, I once suffered from the same complaint myself. Nurse's remedy for this was a bread poultice. To me the application of the poultice on the boil was the most painful part of the operation: it was so very boiling hot. Nevertheless, the old bread poultice was very effective and would draw the core of the boil out completely. One seldom hears of boils today.

In 1960, mother had the honour of attending the Conference of the International Confederation of Midwives to represent the Welsh midwives. This took place in Rome. I have kept her own copy of the souvenir banquet programme. An orchestra played before and during the meal and the programme also included a sophisticated fashion parade, arranged by 'La Gregariana' (Figure 24).

On her return home, mother said very little about the trip, although it had been her first, and only, journey overseas. I don't think that she was very impressed. When I went to Gobowen railway station to meet her from the train, I asked if she had enjoyed herself. Her only comment was that she preferred Cefncoch (her favourite upland countryside west of Llanfair town)!

For some years mother had been sniffing Piton powder to counteract her Drinking Diabetes (mentioned earlier in Chapter 3). Eventually, this went on her lungs and she passed away on February 25 1964 – whilst, as is often said, still 'in harness'. After mother's death large numbers of letters and cards of condolence arrived. As the following extracts show, all reflected the high esteem that she had earned through her work.

From Lilian Roberts of Montford Bridge, Shropshire, a former patient:

'During these sad days I hope your sorrow will be eased by the knowledge that she lived a good life, enjoying the respect and affection of all who came in contact with her and she will long be remembered. I myself have missed a very good friend, she was always so kind to me'.

From Doreen Wilson of Bryn Llewelyn, Newtown, then the Chief Nursing Officer for Montgomeryshire, who, as mentioned in Chapter 3, Mam once took to Gorsdyfwch at Cefncoch to demonstrate the challenges of nursing in a remote community:

'I know how much this loss will mean to the whole district of Llanfair which she served so faithfully for so many years. In fact her work was her life and her people have lost a true friend and comforter'.

From Mr M. J. Evans and family, of Llanfair town:

'I have known your mother for so many years and admired her. She was not only a wonderful nurse, who excelled in her work, but she became a dear friend to many hundreds'.

From J. Mary Pryce, Tre Llydiart, Montgomery, formerly the District Medical Officer:

'I cannot imagine Llanfair without her. It is nearly twenty-five years since I first met her. As the years have gone by, I have realised more and more her extreme kindness and humanity; and also her courage and greatness of spirit. Nothing daunted her and nothing was too much trouble for her. It must be some consolation to you that she died as she would have wished: whilst still 'in harness'. We will be poorer for her loss'.

From Mrs W. H. Davies of Westminster Drive, Wrexham, a member of an old established Llanfair family:

'I can't think of Llanfair without Nurse and I know her passing will be mourned by great numbers of people far and wide. I shall never forget her unfailing goodness to us as a family'.

From Pam Gracey (née Pequignot) of Curzon Park, Chester, one of the evacuees who came to Llanfair town in the early years of the war:

> 'There must be many hundreds of folk, especially around Llanfair district, who will always remember her with respect; and with a high regard for the way she carried out her work, particularly in the severe weather when, even the stoutest of hearts, must have quailed at the thought of journeying to remote farms and cottages'.

From Dr Felix Richards, Montgomeryshire's County Medical Officer of Health:

> 'The unassuming role and devotion she showed in her post was an example to all and one was often reminded of how much she was admired and respected by all who knew her. She will be greatly missed by the community she served for so long and so selflessly'.

From the Rev. D. Arthur Morgan of Machynlleth, formerly Minister of Bethesda, the Wesleyan Methodist Chapel:

> 'Nurse Evans had been a great figure in the life of Llanfair and District for many years. Most devoted to her work, she did her best to all classes of the community to relieve suffering wherever she was called. She was very kind to me always and we mourn a great friend for she was a friend of all'.

From Hilda Williams, of Minsterly, Salop, who once lived in Llanfair:

> 'The whole district has lost one that has served them most faithfully all these years and all will miss her'.

From B. Arfor Williams, Secretary of Bethesda Wesleyan Methodist Chapel of which mother was a trustee:

> 'Please accept a few words on behalf of the Church of which she had been a most loving and hard-working member. Indeed, everyone for a very wide area will feel that part of their lives has now gone forever in the passing of their dear, familiar District Nurse'.

The large number of mourners at her funeral was to be exceeded by the even larger numbers attending the Memorial Service for her some time later. But, by the very nature of their work, it does not do for nurses to show emotions and mother was no exception. Because of the ways she controlled her feelings, to many she may have appeared to be quite hard on the surface. However, three particular events would always bring a tremble to her voice and a tear to her eye. To mother these were deeply sad events concerned with tragic deaths in different circumstances.

The first was the sad story of Edith Cavell, the British nurse who remained in Brussels after the German occupation in 1915, helping to smuggle allied troops to the Dutch border. Nurse Cavell was caught by the Germans and executed by firing squad. The second concerned the traumatic experiences of the bard Hedd Wyn (Ellis Humphrey Evans of Trawsfynydd, Meirionethshire, 1887-1917), now part of Welsh history. Ellis was a young Welsh soldier serving in France during the First World War and he had entered a poem in the Birkenhead Chair Eisteddfod, under the pseudonym 'Hedd Wyn'. As is the custom, the winner of the Chair is called out so that he/she can be acknowledged. However, Hedd Wyn had been killed in action. So, a black cloth was draped over the empty bardic chair on the Eisteddfod platform. This Eisteddfod is still known as 'Eisteddddfod Y Cadair Ddu' (the Eisteddfod of the Black Chair).

Our home, Brynteg, in High Street in Llanfair, adjoined the parish churchyard and the epitaph on one of the headstones there was the third source of grief for mother. From a very young age I was shown this memorial, which records the death, in childbirth, of Ann, wife of Richard Morgan, and daughter of Richard and Martha Richards of the Boot Inn, Llanfair, who died on December 10 1860. The verse has stuck in my memory; and any visitors to our house were told about it:

'Twenty six years I was a maid,
And two years I was a wife,
Two hours I was a mother,
And then I lost my life'.

I am sure that these three events had a great impact on mother's attitude to helping others – especially the last one. Mam would spare no effort to ensure that a mother and her child would be healthy and have every chance of survival. On reflection, because Nurse mentioned the verse on that headstone so frequently, its implications became a sort of crusade for her throughout her professional life.

If someone had passed away without suffering pain, mother's words of comfort would be, 'Croesodd yr afon yn y man culaf' [They have crossed the river at its narrowest point]. Another couplet often quoted by mother was 'Mae dywyll nos a Duw yn well, na golau dydd a Duw ymhell' [The darkness of night with a God, is better than the light of day without a God]. These words, I am sure, gave her great comfort, especially when she was alone on dark nights in remote areas attending a confinement.

Whenever she received such a callout, generally it occurred during the hours of darkness; and often in inclement weather. On many occasions the latter part of her journey had to be completed on foot. Throughout much of her career as Llanfair's District Nurse, mother worked closely with our local doctor, Dr Milton Jones and his partners, to render devoted service to our local community. And, after his retirement, mother continued to work with his son, Dr John Milton Jones – still known by everyone today simply as 'Doctor John'.

The week before she entered hospital, where eventually Mam was to die, she was in a very poor state of health but she insisted on going to see one of her patients. Probably this person was in a better state of health than mother. My father, my brother, and I, all refused to drive her to see this patient because we considered that she was too ill herself to travel. After we had all left the house, mother called a neighbour to drive her to see the patient – such was her dedication.

There are many more instances of her dedication and kindness that have not been recorded. Occasionally, as happened when I was preparing this book, I am still approached by people, some whom I don't really know, who provide yet more anecdotes concerning the Nurse. Recently, I talked with Mr Maurice Bowen of Llwyn Einion, Llanfair, who had been one of the people who had helped mother to mount the ladder to the top of the load of hay during the rough winter of 1947. He told me that they advised Nurse not to go because it was too dangerous as the weather was deteriorating rapidly. Mr Bowen recalled that the men did everything they could to dissuade Nurse from making that journey. Mother's sharp reply summed up her dedication to her profession: 'I must go. It is my duty'.

It was mother's wish that, following her death, her remains should be cremated and her ashes spread on the hills, which lie beyond her beloved Cefncoch. We complied with her wishes and it seems fitting that her remains rest in her favourite place.

Appendices:

The

Llanfair and District Nursing Association.

⸗

(Affiliated with the County Nursing Association).

⸗

RULES and FEES.

R. A. Bryan, Printer, Llanfyllin

A. The Llanfair and District Nursing Association: Rules and Fees.

RULES AND FEES.

1. *The Scale of Fees and Subscriptions will be as follows:—*

Class I. **Old Age Pensioners** and Persons in receipt of Parish Relief shall receive the services of the Nurse **Free of Charge.**

Class II. LABOURERS: A Subscription of 2/- per annum for each family will entitle to 10 free visits, and further visits at 6d. per visit. Non-Subscribers will pay 9d. per visit.

Class III. ARTISANS and FARMERS (holding under 20 acres): Subscription of 3/- per annum entitles to 10 free visits, and further visits at 9d. per visit. Non-Subscribers 1/- per visit.

Class IV. TRADESPEOPLE and FARMERS (holding from 21 to 60 acres): Subscription of 4/- per annum entitles to 10 free visits, and further visits at 1/- per visit. Non-Subscribers 1/3 per visit.

Class V. **Persons not coming under Classes I—IV:** Subscribers, 1/6; Non-Subscribers, 2/6 per visit.

2. **MATERNITY CASES :** The Nurse will be a trained Midwife, and will attend Confinement Cases, and make 10 further visits for the following extra fees :—

Class II. 12/6 for Subscribers; further visits 6d. each. Non-Subscribers, 17/6 ; and 1/- for each further visit.

Class III. 15/- for Subscribers; further visits 6d. each. Non-Subscribers, 20/. ; and 1/- for each further visit.

Class IV. 20/- for Subscribers; further visits 1/- each. Non-Subscribers, 25/- ; and 1/6 for each further visit.

———

In all the above Classes an Extra Fee of 2/- will be charged for a Case which is beyond a radius of one mile from Llanfair.

The Nurse shall have two months' notice in all Maternity Cases, and Subscribers will always have preference over Non-Subscribers.

The Nurse will be responsible for the collection of all Fees which must be paid immediately on the termination of Attendance.

LAST OFFICES :

Classes II and III: Subscribers, 7/6;
Non-Subscribers, 10/-

Classes IV and V: Subscribers, 7/6;
Non-Subscribers, 12/6

3. In any case of illness, if the Nurse wishes for a Doctor, the patient's friends must send for one at once.

4. The Nurse will attend only urgent cases on Sundays.

5. The Nurse will not attend cases of infectious illness without the sanction of the Emergency Committee, and the approval of the Doctor.

6. Applications for the Nurse's Services, must be made to the Nurse herself or to the Secretary.

7. The Nurse shall keep a Register of her visits and engagements and report to the Secretary once a week.

8. If the services of the Nurse are required at night, a trustworthy person should be sent for her with a conveyance, if possible, if the distance is over a mile.

9. Night duty is only to be expected of the Nurse in critical cases.

10. The Nurse shall prepare such nourishment as is required for the patient, and instruct the friends of the patient how to prepare the same. When attending a labourer's wife, where no servant is kept, the Nurse is expected to do all that is required for the patient.

11. In all cases it is the duty of the Nurse to see to all that concerns the bed and person of the patient; to see that the room and all the utensils in it are clean, to use disinfectants when necessary and explain their importance to the family; to see that the room is thoroughly ventilated and to do her best to improve the surroundings of her patient.

12. The Nurse shall be entitled to two weeks' holiday a year, and one day during each month, if her duties permit. The Nurse must report to the Secretary when she is away.

The Llanfair District
Nursing Association.

(Affiliated with the County Nursing Association).

President:

MRS. J. C. HILTON.

Vice-Presidents:

Mrs. E. R. PICKMERE.   Miss HOWELLS.

Hon. Treasurer:

Mrs. THOMAS, Broneinion.

Hon. Secretary:

Mrs. C. E. HUMPHREYS.

Emergency Committee:

Mrs. ELLIS, Mrs. THOMAS, Mrs. TOM JONES, Mrs. C. E. HUMPHREYS.

Executive Committee:

Mrs. C. W. Humphreys.	Mrs. Garfitt.
Mrs. Samuel Ellis.	Mrs. Collins.
Mrs. W. L. Richards.	Mrs. Thomas, Broneinion.
Mrs. Noel Turner.	Mrs. Tom Jones.
Mrs. J. C. Jones.	Mrs. Buckley.
Mrs. Williams, Penarth.	Mrs. Lewis Jones.
Mrs. Humphreys (N.P. Bank).	Mrs. C. E. Humphreys.
Miss Jones, Rhosaflo.	Dr. J. W. Anderson.
Dr. Humphreys.	Dr. Thomas.
Mr. W. Alford Jehu.	

The President, Vice-Presidents, Hon. Treasurer, Hon. Secretary, are Ex-officio Members.

R. A. Bryan, Printer, Llanfyllin.

B. Llanfair District Nursing Association Annual Report and List of Subscriptions 1917-18.

LLANFAIR DISTRICT NURSING ASSOCIATION.

REPORT FOR 1917--18.

I beg to submit the Sixth Annual Report of this Association.

During the year 1917-18 the Nurse attended the following Cases : Medical, 20 ; Surgical, 17 ; Maternity, 9 ; Tuberculosis, 3. These necessitated 555 Visits.

Health Visiting : As Health Visitor the Nurse made 176 visits.

Schools : 29 visits were made to the Elementary Schools in the District and 101 children inspected, while 76 defective children were visited in their homes.

Total number of visits to all cases 1,669, as compared with 1,215 during the previous year.

Maternity : As several of the present registered Midwives are about to retire on account of advancing years, the work of the Nurse in this direction will be greatly increased in the future.

Nurse Gethin is most energetic and tactful in her work and is becoming more appreciated in the district and deserves every encouragement.

J. HUMPHREYS,
Hon. Sec.

LIST OF SUBSCRIPTIONS.

LLANFAIR (In Town).

Collectors—Mrs. Roberts and Miss Ella Morris.

	£	s.	d.
Mrs. Humphreys, Mount Einion	1	1	0
Mrs. Jones, Goat Hotel	0	2	6
Mr. J. Lloyd Peate	0	2	6
Sergt. Hughes	0	1	0
Dr. Thomas	0	10	6
Mr. J. Lloyd Jehu	0	2	6
Mrs. Jones, Bodeinion	0	5	0
Mr. Evans, Brynawel	0	1	0
Mr. and Mrs. Collins	0	7	6
Mr. Levi Jones	0	1	0
Mr. Edwards, Saddler	0	2	6
Mrs. Williams, Corner Shop	0	2	0
Mr. Bennet, Shoemaker	0	1	0
Mrs. S. Ellis, Stone Cottage	0	10	0
Messrs. C. Humphreys & Son	0	10	6
Mr. E. Lloyd Edwards	0	2	6
Mr. Evan Morris, Butcher	0	2	6
Mr. D. Lewis, Draper	0	1	0
Mr. Lewis Jones, L. C. & M. Bank	0	5	0
Mr. D. Astley, Draper	0	2	0
Mr. Evan Owen Evans	0	2	6
Mr. Thomas, Draper	0	1	0
Mr. Davies, Station Master	0	2	0
Mr. C. W. Humphreys, Ty-lissa	0	5	0
Mrs. Howells, Glyn...	0	0	6
Mrs. Jones, Hengefn	0	2	0
Rev. W. Pryce, Brynmair	0	2	0
Mr. Humphreys, N. P. Bank	0	2	6
Mr. Jones, B.A., County School	0	4	0

£5 15 0

Gelligason-in-Town and Brynelen.

Collectors—Mrs. Thomas and Miss Katie Edwards.

Rev. J. E. Rowlands	0	10	6
Mr. Hughes, M.R.C.V.S.	0	5	0
Mrs. Morris, Red Lion	0	2	0
Mrs. W. Astley	0	2	0
Mrs. Large	0	2	0
Mrs. W. Jones, Grocer	0	2	0
Mrs. Jehu	0	3	0
Miss Jones, Grocer	0	1	0
Mrs. Gittins	0	2	0
Mr. J. W. Ellis	0	2	6

	£	s.	d.
Mr. David Davies ...	0	5	0
Mr. Ellis, Chemist ...	0	5	0
Mr. Watkins, Registrar	0	1	0
Mr. Alfred Watkin ...	0	1	0
Rev. W. Thomas ...	0	2	6
Miss Williams, B.A.	0	2	6
Mr. Jehu, Black Lion	0	2	6
Mr. Thomas Richards	0	1	0
Mrs. Jones, Pant-y-bedol	0	0	6
Mrs. Rowlands ...	0	0	6
Mr. Morgan, Eithnog Farm	0	2	0
Mrs. Evans, Brynelen	0	2	0
Mrs. Thomas, Brynelen	0	2	0
Miss Williams, Brynelen	0	1	0
Miss Jones, Brynpistyll	0	2	0
Mr. Astley, Bungalow	0	1	0
	£3	3	6

Gelligason District.

Collector—Miss Buckley.

	£	s.	d.
Mrs. Buckley, Mount Farm	0	5	0
Miss Wood, Pear Tree	0	2	0
Mrs. Edwards, Tynewydd ...	0	2	6
Mrs. Davies, Cilhaul	0	2	0
Mrs. Thomas, Cwmgoleu ...	0	2	0
Mrs. Evans, Yew Tree	0	2	0
Mrs. Owen, Beech Grove	0	1	0
Mrs. Davies, Bryntirion	0	1	0
Miss Jones, Fir Bank	0	1	0
Mr. Emberton, Pencoed	0	1	0
Mrs. Thomas, The Cwm	0	1	0
Mrs. Astley, Tynyberwydd...	0	1	0
Mrs. Owen, Rhywgoch	0	1	0
Mrs. Bebb, The Wells	0	1	0
Miss Thomas, Rhosfawr	0	1	0
Mr. Marsh, Red House	0	0	6
Miss Parry, Ochor ...	0	0	3
A Friend	0	0	3
Mrs. Lewis, Gelligason	0	1	0
	£1	6	6

Llanoddian Upper.

Collector—Miss N. Rice-Jones.

	£	s.	d.
Mrs. Jones, Pentre ...	0	2	0
Mr. Evans, Caellewelyn	0	2	6
Mrs. Evans, Bronygarth	0	2	6
Miss Pryce, Bethlehem	0	1	0
Mrs. Jones, Graigwen	0	0	6
Mrs. Thomas, Graigwen	0	1	0

				£	s.	d.
Mr. Jones, Llanoddian	...	...	..	0	2	0
Mr. Norman Jones, Gwynyndy	...	...	...	0	5	0
Mrs. Jones, Caeberllan	...	...	...	0	5	0
Mr. Jones, Neuadd :..	...	...	...	0	2	0
Misses Davies, Dolgoch	...	...	...	0	1	0
Mr. Jehu, Bronavon	...	...	...	0	5	0
Mrs. Morris, Vyrnwy Villa	...	...	...	0	2	0
Mrs. Rhys Lewis ...	...	...	...	0	2	6
Mrs. Roberts, Dolgoch	...	...	...	0	0	6

£1 14 6

Pentyrch District.

Collector—Mrs. Jones, Pentyrch.

Mrs. Roberts, Cefndre	...	...	...	0	2	6
Mr. David Roberts ...	...	...	...	0	1	0
Mr. Edwin Rees ...	...	...	...	0	0	6
Mr. Edgar Jones ...	...	...	...	0	0	3
Miss Bebb, Hendre	...	...	...	0	2	0
Mr. T. Jerman ...	...	...	...	0	1	0
Miss Watkins, Rhos	...	...	...	0	2	0
Mr. Jones, Bryndu ...	...	...	...	0	2	0
Mr. Gittins, Erwfanadl	...	...	...	0	2	0
Mrs. Roberts, Coedcaehaidd	...	...	...	0	1	0
Mr. Williams, Coedcaehaidd bach	...	...	...	0	2	0
Mr. Bourne, Brickyard	...	...	...	0	2	0
Miss Jones, Tycoch ...	..	...	...	0	2	0
Miss Evans, Tynewydd	...	...	...	0	2	0
Miss Gittins, Tanyfoel	...	...	...	0	1	0
Mr. Francis Jones ...	...	...	...	0	0	6
Mrs. Jones, Pentyrch	...	...	...	0	2	0

£1 5 9

Rhiwhiriaeth District.

Collector—Miss Davies, Cefnypark.

Mr. E. Rees, Cross Farm ...	...	...	...	0	2	0
Mrs. Williams, Rhiwhiraeth	...	...	...	0	2	0
Miss Evans, Middle Rhiwhiraeth ...		...	...	0	2	0
Miss Jones, Tymawr	...	...	...	0	2	0
Mrs. Hinsley, Dolglenyn	...	...	...	0	1	6
Mrs. Jones, Old Smithy	...	...	..	...	0	1	0
Mrs. Baines Thomas	...	...	...	0	1	0
Mrs. H. Evans, Melinddol ...	...	...	...	0	2	0
Mrs. Hamer, School House	...	...	...	0	2	0
Mrs. Tudor, Pantglenyn	...	...	...	0	1	0
Mrs. Owen, Tyucha ...	...	...	...	0	1	0

£0 17 6

Brynglas and Dolgead.

Collectors—Miss Jones, Penybryn, Miss Griffiths, Brynglas Hall.

				£	s.	d.
Mrs. Jones, Penybryn	...	...	...	...	0	2	6
Mrs. Griffiths, Gartheilin	...	...	...	...	0	2	6
Mrs. Roberts, Brynglas Hall		...	...	...	0	2	0
Mrs. Evans, Brynglas	...	...	...	...	0	2	0
Miss Lloyd, Tyddyn	...	...	...	...	0	2	0
Miss Davies, Fronhaul	...	...	...	...	0	1	0
Mrs. Jones, Rhydarwydd	...	...	...	...	0	1	0
Mr. Jervis, Dolgead	...	...	...	...	...	0	2	6
Mrs. Evans, Dolgead Ucha		...	...	...	0	1	0

£0 16 6

Penarth.

Collectors—Miss Dilys Humphreys, Miss Maggie Jehu.

Mrs. Jones, Penllan ...	...	...	...	...	0	0	6
Miss Davies, Vron	...	...	...	...	0	2	0
Mrs. Jones, White Lane	...	...	...▪	...	0	2	0
Mrs. Breeze, Penybont	...	...	...	...	0	1	0
Mrs. Buckley, Tynycelyn	...		...	...	0	1	0
Miss Hughes, Maespryd	...	...	...	...	0	0	6
Mrs. Jones, Brynmawr	...	...	...	...	0	1	0
Mrs. Jones, Glog	...	...	...	...	...	0	1	0
Mr. Whittaker, Brynrhug	...	...	...	...	0	1	0
Mrs. Morris, Gaer	...	...	...	...	0	1	0
Mrs. Davies, Llwyngwyn	...	...	...	...	0	2	0
Mrs, Lewis, Tygwyn	...	...	...	...	0	1	0
Mrs. Astley, Cwmllwyngwyn		...	...	...	0	0	6
Mrs. Astley, Caerwedin	...	...	...	...	0	1	0
Mrs. Davies, Adwywynt	...	...	...	...	0	1'	0
Mrs. Phillips, Bronfedw	...	...	...	...	0	2	6
Mrs. Jones, Penarth	...	...	...	...	0	2	0
Mrs. Humphreys, Penrhiew		...	...	...	0	2	0
Mrs. Thomas, Mount Pleasant	...	...	.	0	2	0
Mrs. Davies, Pentre	...	...	...	...	0	1	0
Mrs. Davies, Bryn Penarth	...	...	...	0	1	0
Mr. Morris, Bryn Penarth	...	...	...	...	0	1	0

£1 8 0

Heniarth.

Collectors—Miss Gittins, Heniarth, Miss Thomas, Brynclen.

Mrs. Jones, Tanllan	...	...	...	...	0	2	0
Mrs. Gittins, Heniarth	...	...	...	...	0	2	0
Mr. Jones, Dolrhyd ...	...	...	...	...	0	1	0
Misses Thomas, Tanybryn ...		...	...	...	0	0	6

£0 5 6

Rhosaflo.

Collectors—Miss Davies, Neuadd, Miss Griffiths, Brynglas Hall.

	£	s.	d.
Mrs. Evans, Cwmllwynog	0	2	0
Mrs. Jones, Rhosaflo	0	2	0
Mrs. Davies, Neuadd	0	1	0
Mrs. Richards, Allt Ucha	0	1	0
Mrs. Watkins, Pantgwyn	0	1	0
Mrs. Bebb, Maesyglydfa	0	1	0
Mrs. Rees, Tynllwyn	0	1	0
Mrs. Jones, Brynrefel	0	0	6
Mrs. Morgan, Wern	0	1	0
	£0	10	6

Llangyniew District.

Collectors—Miss Roberts, Glascoed, Miss Lloyd, Tymawr.

	£	s.	d.
Rev W. L. Richards	0	10	6
Mrs. Jones, Tyddyn	0	2	6
Mrs. Griffiths, School House	0	2	6
Mrs. Jerman, Henllan	0	2	6
Mrs. Adams, Henllan	0	1	0
Mrs. Lloyd, Tymawr	0	3	0
Mrs. James, Tanyffridd	0	2	0
Mrs. Harris, Tanhouse	0	5	0
Mrs. Wooding	0	2	0
	£1	11	0

Llangyniew District.

Collectors—Miss Adams, Miss Brown, Tynywern.

	£	s.	d.
Mrs. Brown, Tynywern	0	2	0
Mrs. Davies, Tybrith	0	2	0
Mrs. Humphreys, Pentrecoed	0	2	0
Mrs. Jones, Henllan Mill	0	1	0
Mrs. Haynes, Caethle	0	1	0
Mrs. Griffiths, Heniarth Mill ..:	0	2	0
Mrs. Bebb, Glascoed	0	2	0
Mrs. Fox, Glascoed Cottage	0	1	0
Mrs. Jepson, Glascoed	0	2	0
Mrs. Jones, Pen Pentre	0	2	6
Mrs. Jones, Pentre	0	2	0
Mrs. Nutting, Pentre	0	2	6
Mrs. Bebb, Cefnllwyd	0	2	0
	£1	4	0

Llanfair District Nursing Association.—Treasurer's Statement for year ending 31st March, 1918.

RECEIPTS.	£	s.	d.	£	s.	d.
Balance in hand, 31st March, 1917				31	13	8
Subscriptions and Donations:						
J. C. Hilton, Esq.	3	0	0			
Mr. and Mrs. Garfitt	2	2	0			
Miss Howell	2	0	0			
Mrs. Pickmere	0	10	0			
Mr. and Mrs. Collin	0	10	0	8	2	0
Llanfyllin Guardians	2	2	0			
Education Authority Grant	10	0	0			
King Edward Memorial	5	0	0			
Health Visiting Grant	5	0	0			
Castle Caereinion Charity	1	0	0	23	2	0
Subscriptions collected in Districts	18	13	9			
Congregational Church (two years)	1	7	0			
Wesleyan Church	0	16	0			
Calviniatic Methodist Church	1	1	0			
Parish Church (two years)	2	5	6	24	3	3
Proceeds of Concert				29	7	0
Patients' Fees				11	14	6
Bank Interest				0	11	0
				£128	13	5

PAYMENTS.	£	s.	d.
Nurse Gethin—Salary	78	0	0
Insurance	0	13	0
Postages	0	2	3
Charts	0	1	0
Garroulds	2	0	5
Mr. H. E. Ellis	1	3	3
Mr. E. Lloyd Edwards—Nurse's Dresses	1	16	7
Mrs. C. E. Humphreys—Bed-rest	1	0	0
Bicycle Repairs	2	4	3
Affiliation Fees	0	10	6
Cheque Book	0	4	2
Hire of Hall for Concert	1	10	0
Printing of Tickets	0	7	0
Hire of Committee Room	0	12	0
	90	4	5
Balance in hand	38	9	0
	£128	13	5

Examined and found correct, 8th April, 1918—M. LEWIS JONES, Hon. Auditor.

(Signed) EDITH OWEN THOMAS, Hon. Treasurer.

The Llanfair District Nursing Association.

(Affiliated with the County Nursing Association).

PRESIDENT:

W. ALFORD JEHU, ESQ., J.P.

PRESIDENT OF EXECUTIVE COMMITTEES:

MRS. E. R. PICKMERE.

VICE-PRESIDENT OF EXECUTIVE COMMITTEES:

MRS. LEWIS JONES.

HON. TREASURER:

Mrs. THOMAS, Broneinion.

HON. SECRETARY:

Miss M. PULESTON JONES.

EMERGENCY COMMITTEE:

Mrs. Ellis, Mrs. Thomas, Mrs. Tom Jones, Miss M. Puleston Jones.

EXECUTIVE COMMITTEE:

Mrs. C. W. Humphreys.	Mrs. Heber Humphreys.
Mrs. Samuel Ellis.	Mrs. D. R. Thomas.
Mrs. Lloyd Williams.	Mrs. Puleston Jones.
Mrs. T. Lewis, N. P. Bank.	Mrs. W. Metcalfe.
Miss Jones, Rhiwhiriaith.	Mrs. Milton Jones.
Mrs. Tom Jones.	Mrs. Roberts, Llangyniew Rectory.
Mrs. Buckley.	Mrs. W. Astley.
Mrs. W. Thomas.	Miss M. Puleston Jones.
Miss Corbett, Cefngoleu.	

REPORT FOR 1921--22.

I beg to submit the Tenth Annual Report of this Association.

During the year 1921-22 the Nurse attended the following Cases :— Medical, 21 ; Surgical, 20 ; Maternity, 38 ; Tuberculosis, 7. These necessitated 1,436 visits.

Health Visiting: As Health Visitor the Nurse made 194 visits.

Schools : Twenty-five visits were made to the Elementary Schools in the District, and 64 visits to children's homes.

Total number of visits to all cases 1,436, as compared with 1,078 during the previous year.

Nurse Mills is most energetic in her work and deserves every appreciation.

M. PULESTON JONES, Hon. Sec.

R. A. BRYAN, PRINTER, LLANFYLLIN.

C. Llanfair District Nursing Association Annual Report and List of Subscriptions 1921-22.

Llanfair District Nursing Association.--Treasurer's Statement for Year ending March 31st, 1922.

RECEIPTS.

	£	s.	d.	£	s.	d.
Subscriptions and Donations:						
Mrs. Noel Turner	5	0	0			
J. M. Howell, Esq.	5	0	0			
J. C. Hilton, Esq.	2	2	0			
Mr. David Davies	1	18	6			
Mrs. J. C. Jones	1	0	0			
Mrs. W. L. Richards	1	0	0			
Mrs. Metcalfe	1	0	0	17	1	6
Grants:						
Nurse's Salary Augmentation	10	0	0			
Health Visiting	10	0	0			
Local Education Authority	12	0	0			
Welsh National Memorial	5	0	0			
Board of Guardians	2	2	0			
Castle United Charities	1	0	0			
Ministry of Health	4	0	0	44	2	0
Collections in Places of Worship:						
Parish Church	1	19	7			
Moriah C. M. Chapel	1	1	0			
Congregational Chapel	0	13	9			
Subscriptions collected in District	3	14	4			
Patients' Fees	42	8	0			
Bank Interest	33	19	6			
	1	7	0	142	12	4
Balance in hand April 1st, 1921				70	11	8
				£213	4	0

PAYMENTS.

	£	s.	d.	£	s.	d.
Nurse's Salary	100	18	0			
,, Postages	0	4	0	100	17	0
Drugs and Dressings	6	6	1			
New Bicycle	11	0	1			
Nurse's Uniform	11	15	11			
Postages	0	12	0			
Nurse's Cupboard	4	5	0			
Affiliation Fee	0	10	6			
Nursing Bags	0	7	11			
Case Book	0	5	0			
Cheque Books	0	8	4	85	10	9
				186	7	9
Balance in Bank				76	16	3
				£213	4	0

(*Signed*) EDITH OWENA THOMAS, Hon. Treasurer.
MAURICE LEWIS JONES, Hon. Auditor.

LLANFAIR (In Town).

Collectors—Miss Hughes, Bon Marche and Miss Lloyd Edwards.

	£	s.	d.
Mrs. Lewis Jones, L. C. &. M. Bank	1	1	0
Mr. M. Lewis Jones „	0	10	0
Mr. and Mrs. Lewis, N. P. Bank	0	10	6
Mrs. Humphreys Mount Einion	0	10	0
Dr. Milton Jones	0	10	0
Mrs. Ellis, Stone House	0	10	0
Mrs. Thomas, Bryn Glas Cottage	0	2	0
Mr. and Mrs. Humphreys Ty-lissa	0	6	0
Mrs. Jones, Hengefn	0	2	0
Mrs. Astley, Tanhouse	0	1	0
Mrs. Tom Davies, Watergate St.	0	2	0
Mrs. Thomas, Chapel House	0	2	0
Mr. Bennett, Gwynfa	0	2	6
Mrs. R. Davies, Poplars	0	2	6
Mrs. Tudor, Tanyfron	0	3	0
Mrs. McCabe	0	2	0
Mr. and Mrs. Owen, Weston House	0	4	0
Mrs. Williams, Corner Shop	0	4	0
Mr. L. Roberts	0	1	0
Mr. E. Lloyd Edwards	0	5	0
Mrs. Jones, The Goat	0	2	6
Mr. Peate, Fair View	0	2	6
Mrs. Evans, Islwyn	0	4	0
Mrs. E. Bennett, Rose Cottage	0	4	0
Mrs. Bolver	0	2	0
Mrs. Jones, Bodeinion	0	5	0
Mr. Collins, Bryn Llywelyn	0	7	6
Mrs. Davies, Ty Mawr	0	2	6
Mr. and Mrs. Pierce	0	2	0
Mrs. Evans, Brynawel	0	5	0
Mrs. Evans, Banw House	0	3	0
Miss Morgan, Bodlondeb	0	2	6
Mrs. Jones, Bodeinion Cottage	0	1	0
Mrs. Davies, Crown House	0	2	6
Mr. and Mrs. Anwyl Evans	0	2	6
Mrs. Jones, Temperance	0	2	0
Sergeant Hughes	0	2	0
Mrs. D. Peate	0	5	0
Mr. and Mrs. Edwards, Saddler	0	5	0
Mrs. Fred Jones	0	2	0
Rev. and Mrs. D. R. Thomas.	0	4	0
Mrs. Davies, Glasgow House	0	4	0
Mrs. Breeze, Swan	0	2	0
Mrs. Lewis, Draper	0	2	0

				£	s.	d.
Mrs E. Morris, Butcher	...	...	...	o	5	o
Mrs. Bailey Williams	...	...	...	o	5	o
Mrs. Astley, Bungalow, Hassal Yard	...		...	o	1	o
Mrs. J. Astley	...	...	...	o	2	o
Mrs. Llewelyn Jehu...	...	...	...	o	1	o
Mrs. Bumford	...	...	...	o	1	o
Mrs. Humphrey Tudor	...	...	...	o	2	o
Mrs. Evans, Tailor ...	...	...	...	o	1	o
Mrs. Jones, Bodeinion Villa	...	...	...	o	2	o
Mrs. Evan Evans, Swan Yard		...	...	o	4	o
Mrs. Morris, Temperance	...	...	...	o	2	6
Mrs. Bye ...	...	...	...	o	4	o
Miss Ellis, Watergate Street ...		...	...	o	2	o
Mr. and Mrs. Roberts, L. C. & M. Bank			...	o	2	6
Mrs. Davies, Star Shop	...	...	...	o	2	o
Mr. Thomas, Draper	...	...	...	o	2	6
Mrs. Jones, Holly House	...	...	...	o	2	o
Mrs. Hughes, Bon Marche	...	...	...	o	4	o
Mrs. Evans, Rathbone House		...	...	o	4	o
Mr. Astley, Tailor ...	...	...	...	o	4	o
Mr. E. Davies, Bridge Street...		...	...	o	1	o
Mr. Lloyd, Watchmaker	...	...	...	o	1	o
Mr. J. Lloyd Jehu ...	...	...	...	o	4	o
Miss Roberts, County School...		...	...	o	2	o
Mrs. Barker, Bridge Street	...	...	...	o	1	o
Mrs. James, The Institute	...	...	...	o	3	o
Mrs. Millington	...	...	...	o	1	o
Mrs. Puleston Jones	...	...	...	o	7	6

£12 19 o

Gelligasson-in-Town and Brynelen.

Collectors— Mrs. W. Thomas and Miss M. Puleston Jones.

Rev. J. E. Rowlands	...	...	...	o	5	o
Mr. C. Edgington ...	...	...	...	o	5	o
Mrs. Jehu, Black Lion	...	...	...	o	5	o
Mr. Astley, Bungalow	...	...	...	o	2	o
Mr. Thomas Richards	...	..	...	o	o	6
Mrs. Jones, Whitehall	...	..	...	o	1	o
Mrs. Large, Bee Hive Stores		...	...	o	4	o
Mrs. W. Astley	...	...	...	o	4	o
Mrs. Morris, Red Lion	...	...	...	o	4	o
Mr. W. Jones, Grocer	...	...	...	o	4	o
Mrs. Watkin, Stationers	...	..	...	o	1	6
Mrs. Gittins	...	...	...	o	4	o
Rev. and Mrs. W. Thomas	...	...	...	o	6	o
Mrs. W. H. Davies...	...	...	...	o	4	o
Mrs. Alfred Watkins	...	...	...	o	2	o
Mr. Davies, Prince ...	...	...	...	o	5	o
Mr. Morris, Llymustyn	...	...	...	o	2	o

				£	s.	d.
Miss Edwards, Bodhyfryd	...	...	...	0	2	0
Mrs. Cynon Evans	...	...	...	0	3	0
Mrs. Breeze, Wesley Street	...	...	...	0	2	0
Mrs. Sydney Evans	...	...	...	0	2	6
Mrs. Rowlands, Einion Villa	...	...	...	0	2	0
Mrs. Williams, Eithnog Farm		...	...	0	2	6
Mrs. Thomas, Brynelen	...	...	...	0	2	0
Mr. Morgan, Brynelen	...	...	...	0	2	6
Miss Evans, Brynelen	...	...	...	0	1	6
Mrs. Jones, Brynpistyll	...	...	...	0	2	0
Miss Jones, Grocer	...	...	...	0	2	0
				£4	3	0

Gelligason District.

Collectors—Miss Buckley and Miss M. Puleston Jones.

				£	s.	d.
Mr. and Mrs. Pickmere, Mount Hall	...	...	1	1	0
Mrs. Buckley, Mount Farm	...	...	...	0	6	0
Mrs. Griffith, Bryntirion	...	...	...	0	1	0
Mrs. Bebb, The Wells	...	...	...	0	2	0
Miss Hughes, Bank Wells	...	...	...	0	1	0
Mrs. Evans, Yew Tree	...	...	...	0	2	0
Mrs. Owen, Rhiwgoch	...	...	...	0	2	0
Mrs. Edwards, Carreg Arthur		...	...	0	2	0
Mrs. Astley, Tynyberwydd	...	...	...	0	2	0
Mrs. Bowen, Ochor ...	...	...	...	0	2	6
Miss A. Jones, Brynhyfryd	...	...	...	0	1	0
Mrs. Thomas, Tynywern	...	...	...	0	1	0
Mrs. Davies, Lower Cilhaul	...	...	...	0	2	0
Mr. Davies, Upper Cilhaul	...	...	...	0	2	0
Mrs. Thomas, Cwmgoleu	...	...	...	0	3	0
Mrs. Walter Thomas, The Cwm		...	...	0	2	0
Mrs. Watkin, Tygwyn	...	...	...	0	2	0
Miss Thomas, Rhosfawr	...	...	...	0	1	0
Mrs. Marsh, Red House	...	...	...	0	1	0
Mrs. Owen, Beach Grove	...	...	...	0	1	0
Miss Jones, Fir Bank	...	...	...	0	2	6
Miss Wood, Pear Tree	...	...	...	0	2	6
Mrs. Lewis, Gelligason	...	...	...	0	2	6
Mrs. Buckley, Pistyll	...	...	...	0	1	0
				£3	6	0

Llanoddian Upper.

Collectors—Mrs. Metcalfe and Miss I. Davies.

				£	s.	d.
Mr. Alford Jehu, Bronafon	...	...	...	0	10	6
Mr. E. Jones, County School	...	...	...	0	5	0
Mrs. Jones, Cae Berllan	...	...	...	0	5	0
Mr. Norman Jones, Penlan	...	...	...	0	5	0
Mrs. Peate, Glaneinion	...	...	...	0	2	0

	£	s.	d.
Miss L. Williams, Pool Road	o	1	o
Mrs. Davies ,, ...	o	o	6
Mrs. Astley ,, ...	o	o	6
Mrs. Williams ,, ...	o	1	o
Mrs. Whiffin and Mrs. Isaac, Pool Rd. ...	o	2	o
Mr. Frank Jones	o	1	o
Mrs. Roberts	o	1	o
Misses Davies, Dolgoch	o	2	o
Mrs. E. Rowlands	o	2	o
Mrs. Lewis, The Mill	o	4	o
Mrs. Williams, Vyrnwy Villa	o	2	6
Mrs. Wright, Preswylfa	o	2	o
Mr. Jones, Neuadd	o	2	o
Mrs. Williams, Pentre Ucha	o	2	o
Mrs. Jones, Pentre	o	2	o
Miss Price, Bethlehem	o	2	o
Mrs. Thomas, Graigwen	o	1	o
Mrs. Evans, Bronygarth	o	4	o
Mr. Evans, Cae Lleywelyn	o	3	6
Mr. Harold James, Manchester	o	2	6
Mrs. Rice Jones	o	2	o
Mrs. Jones, Gwynyndy	o	4	o
Mrs. Richards, Llanoddian Hall	o	2	6
Mr. FitzPatrick, Manchester...	o	2	6
Paddy Prew	o	1	6
Mrs. Jones, Neuaddlwyd	o	2	6
Mr. Jones, Llanoddian	o	2	o
Mrs. Leah, Pool Rd.	o	o	6
Mrs. Parkes	o	2	o
	£4	5	6

Pentyrch District.

Collector—Mrs. Jones, Pentyrch.

	£	s.	d.
Mrs. Gittins, Tanyfoel	o	5	o
Mrs. Wood, Gelli	o	2	6
Mrs. Llywarch, Coedcaehaidd	o	2	6
Mrs. Jones, Cefndre...	o	5	o
Mr. C. R. Jones	o	1	o
Mr. D. Williams, Coedcaehaidd	o	2	o
Mrs. Jones, Tyngerddi	o	2	o
Mr. Gittins, Erw Fanadl	o	2	6
Mrs. Bebb, Hendre	o	2	6
Mr. Thomas Jones	o	2	o
Miss Watkins, Rhos	o	2	6
Mr. T. Evans, Henefail	o	o	6
Mr. R. Jones, Tyngerddi	o	1	o
	£1	11	o

143

Rhiwhiriaeth District.

Collectors—Miss Jones, Rhiwhiriaeth and Miss K. Pugh, Cilhaul.

			£	s.	d.
Mr. J. Humphreys, Glynhiriaeth	—	...	0	4	0
Mrs. Watkins, Brynhiriaeth ...	...	...	0	5	0
Miss Phillips, Rhiwhiriaeth ...	. .	...	0	2	6
Mrs. Owen, Tyucha... ...	...	...	0	3	0
Mr. E. Morgans, Rhiwhiriaeth Issa	...	...	0	2	6
Mr. H. Morgans ,,	...	...	0	2	6
Mr. A. Breeze, Tynypant ...	...	...	0	2	0
Miss Jones, Tymawr ...	...	...	0	2	6
Mrs. Astley Melinddol ...	...	...	0	2	0
Mrs. Baines Thomas, Melinddol	...	...	0	2	0
Mrs. Ann Evans ,,	...	...	0	2	0
Mrs. David Evans ,,	...	...	0	1	0
Mrs. John Lloyd Jones ,,	...	...	0	2	0
Mrs. Pugh, Cilhaul	...	..	0	4	0
Mrs. Morgan, Melinddol ...	...	...	0	2	0
Mrs. Hinsley Dolgelynen ...	...	...	0	3	0
Mrs. Evans, Pantglas ...	...	...	0	2	0
Mr. Robert Jones, Cross Farm	...	...	0	2	0
Misses Jones, Tynyfawnog ...	...	...	0	2	0
Mrs. Astley, Siloh Chapel House	...	...	0	1	0
Mrs. Evans, Ty Issa ...	...	...	0	2	0
Miss Watkin, Siloh Shop ...	...	...	0	1	6
Mrs. Watkin, Glyn Ucha ...	....	...	0	1	0
Mrs. Watkins, Tanyglyn ..	...	...	0	2	0
Mrs. Jones, Rhiwhiriaeth Ganol	...	...	0	5	0
Mrs. Astley. Tynewydd ...	...	...	0	1	0
Mrs. Jones, Tynywern ...	...	...	0	2	6
Mrs. Jones, Tynywerglodd ...	...	...	0	2	0
Mrs. Davies Parkyrhiw ...	...	...	0	2	6
Mrs. Tudor, Pantygelenyn ..	...	...	0	2	6
Mrs. Williams, Rhiwhiriaeth ...	...	...	0	2	0
Mrs. Hughes, Penyparc ...	...	...	0	2	0
Mrs. Jones, Waenyglapiau. ...	...	...	0	1	0
Mrs. Watkins, Rhosgoch ...	...	...	0	1	0
Mrs. Jones, Lletty	...	...	0	2	6
Mrs. Jaundrell, Penycwm ...	...	...	0	5	0
Mrs. Jones, Nantycae ...	...	...	0	2	0
Mrs. Jones, Tanygraig ...	...	...	0	2	0
Mr. Waters, Pencraig ...	...	...	0	1	0
Mrs. Hughes, Ystrad Fach ...	...	...	0	2	6
Mrs. Watkins, Bryngwewyr ...	...	...	0	2	6
Misses Davies, Bryntawel ...	...	...	0	2	0
Mrs. Williams, Waenybitffel ...	...	...	0	2	0
Mrs. Roberts, Pencroenllwm ...	...	...	0	2	6
Mrs. Evans, Ysguboriau ...	...	...	0	1	0
Mr. Hamer, School House ...	...	...	0	2	6

£5 4 6

Brynglas and Dolgead.

Collectors—Miss Bennett, Dolgead, and Miss Griffith, Gartheilin.

	£	s.	d.		£	s.	d.
Mr. Tom Jervis, Dolgead	0	5	0	Mrs. Roberts, Brynglas Hall	0	2	0
Mrs. Williams, Tawelan	0	3	0	Messrs. D. & J. Roberts ,,	0	2	0
,, Griffiths, Gartheilin	0	3	0	Mrs. Jones, Penybryn	0	2	6
,, Jones, Rhydarwydd	0	2	0	Mr. Lloyd, Tyddyn	0	3	0
,, Davies, Tynrhos	0	2	0	,, Evans, Dolgead	0	1	6
,, Jones, Caenymynydd	0	2	6	Mrs. Jones, Bronhaul	0	2	0
,, Evans, Pensarnunu	0	2	6	Mr. C. Victor Jones, Gartheilin	0	1	0
,, Evans, Tynrhos	0	2	6				
,, Evans, Brynglas	0	3	0		£1	19	6

Penarth.

Collectors—Miss M. Jones, Brynmawr, and Miss Enid Jones, White Lane

	£	s.	d.		£	s.	d.
Mrs. Lloyd Williams, Penarth	0	3	6	Mrs. Davies, Pentre	0	2	6
Mr. Davies, Gaer	0	3	0	,, Jones, Penllan	0	2	6
Mr. Jephson, Plasiolyn	0	3	0	,, Bumford, Pentrecoed	0	2	6
Mrs Humphreys, Penrhiw	0	3	0	,, Lewis, Ty Gwyn	0	2	6
Mr. Davies. Llwyngwyn	0	3	0	Miss Davies, Fron	0	1	0
Mrs, Jones, White Lane	0	2	6	Mrs. Thomas, Mount Pleasant	0	1	0
,, Buckley, Tyn Celyn	0	2	6	Miss Astley, Caerwedyn	0	1	0
,, Jones, Penarth	0	2	6	Mr. Jones, Brynmawr	0	2	6
,, Davies, Adwywynt	0	2	6	Mr. Astley, Caeddolau	0	2	0
,, Phillips, Brynpenarth	0	2	0				
Mr. Morris ,,	0	2	0		£2	7	0

Heniarth.

Collector—Miss Gittins, Heniarth Farm.

	£	s.	d.		£	s.	d.
Mr. & Mrs. Jones, Dolrhyd Mill	0	2	6	Mrs. Gittins, Heniarth	0	5	0
Mrs. Jones, Tanllan	0	2	0	Mr. L. Jones, Tanybryn	0	1	0
Mrs. Jones, Penybryn	0	2	0				
Mrs. Thomas, Tanllan Cottage	0	2	0		£0	14	6

Rhosaflo.

Collectors—Miss Morris, Rhosaflo, and Miss Williams, Penyrwtra.

	£	s.	d.		£	s.	d.
Miss Hughes, Glanbanw	0	5	0	Mrs. Evans, Newadd	0	2	0
,, Evans, Cwmllwynog	0	3	6	,, Roberts, Pentyrch Smithy	0	2	0
Mrs. Jones, Old Smithy	0	2	6	,, Williams, Penyrwtra	0	2	0
Mr. Rowlands, Stingwern	0	2	6	,, Williams, Maes	0	0	6
Mrs. Morgans, Wern	0	2	6	,, Richards, Alltucha	0	1	0
,, Watkins, Pantgwyn	0	2	6	Mr. W. Williams, Allt Isa	0	1	0
,, Rees, Tynllwyn	0	2	6				
,, Williams, Rhosaflo	0	2	6		£1	12	0

Llangyniew.

Collectors—Miss Lloyd, Tymawr, and Miss Violet Evans.

	£	s.	d.		£	s.	d.
Mrs. Thomas, Haulfron	0	10	0	,, Bebb, Glascoed	0	2	6
,, Griffith, School House	0	5	0	,, Fox ,,	0	2	6
,, Griffiths, Heniarth Mill	0	2	6	,, Jephson ,,	0	2	6
,, Astley, Tynwern	0	3	0	,, Williams, Heniarth Gate	0	2	6
,, Jones, Henllan Mill	0	5	0	,, Evans, Glascoed Villa	0	2	0
,, Davies, Ty Brith	0	2	0	Mr. Jones, Pen y Pentre	0	2	6
,, Humphreys, Penybont	0	5	0	,, Jones, Pentre	0	2	6
,, Owen, Lodge	0	2	0	Mrs. Nutting ,,	0	3	6
,, Owen, Pandy	0	2	6	,, Roberts, Cefnllwyd	0	2	0
,, Morris, Henllan	0	3	0	,, Bebb ,,	0	2	6
,, Jones, Henllan Fach	0	2	6	,, Slingsby, Tanhouse	0	2	6
,, Jerman, Henllan	0	2	6	,, Edwards, Trwn	0	2	6
,, Jones, Rectory	0	2	0	,, Haynes, Glascoed Cottage	0	2	0
,, Lloyd, Tymawr	0	4	0				
, Jones, Tyddyn	0	3	0		£4	6	0

Llanfair District Nursing Association

President:
Dr W. MILTON JONES, Cartref.

Hon. Treasurer:
Mrs. I. ANWYL EVANS, Liverpool House.

Hon. Secretary:
Mrs. A. HEWITT, Bron Einion.

Emergency Committee:
Dr. W. Milton Jones, Mrs. Milton Jones. Mrs. I. A. Evans, Mrs
A. Hewitt.

Executive Committee:
Mrs. Morgan, Ystrad; Miss Corbett, Cefn Goleu; Mrs Milton
Jones, Cartref; Mrs. Humphreys, Mount Einion; Mrs. Madryn
Jones, Llys Myfyr; Mrs. J. P. Jones, Caerberllan; Mrs. W.
H. Davies. Birmingham House; Mrs. Hopkins Jones, The
Vicarage; Mrs. H. W. Jones, Frongoch Hall; Mrs. H. D. Owen,
Hafod-y-Gan: Miss A. Threadgold, Cefncoch Hotel; Mrs.
Maendy Jones, Preswylfa, and the Officials.

Nurse's Telephone Number: Llanfair 50.

——o——

REPORT FOR YEAR ENDING MARCH 31st, 1947.

I am pleased to present the 35th Annual Report of the
Llanfair and District Association. The report relates to the
work of our Association during the year ending March 31st,
1947, for which period statements of Accounts are also sub-
mitted. During the year the following cases were attended
by Nurse: Midwifery and Maternity, 27; visits made to these
cases, 378; medical and surgical, 70; visits, 970. As Health
Visitor and sick nursing tuberculosis cases she made 435
visits. Total visits to all cases, 1,783. Visits to schools, 53;
visits to children's homes, 81.

The Committee wish to express thanks to all subscribers
who have generously increased their subscriptions and ap-
peal for an added increase in subscriptions during the following year. The County Association has intimated to the
Health Committee of the County Council its willingness to
assist and co-operate in carrying out the provisions of the
National Health Service Act, 1946, but in the meantime the
District Associations are requested not to relax in their efforts to maintain the nursing services in their areas and as
this cannot be done without an increase in funds my committee appeals for your generous support again this year.
Our thanks are once again extended to Nurse Evans who car-
ries out her work efficiently and conscientiously in the Llanfair area.

H. M. HEWITT,
Secretary.

*D. Llanfair District Nursing Association Annual Report
and List of Subscriptions. 1946-47.*

Statement of Accounts for the Year

RECEIPTS.

	£	s	d	£	s	d
Donations:—						
J. M. Howell, Esq.	1	1	0			
T. Gomer Morris, Esq.	1	1	0			
Mrs. Hopkins Jones (in memory of the late Mrs. David Jehu)	1	1	0			
Mrs. W. B. W. Metcalfe	1	1	0			
				4	4	0
Collections in places of Worship:—						
St. Mary's Church	1	7	6			
Ebenezer Congregational Chapel	0	12	6			
Bethesda Methodist Chapel	1	5	0			
Moriah C.M. Chapel	0	10	0			
				3	15	0
By Sale of part equipment (1st Aid Point)				2	0	0
By Balance of Commission on Rose Hip Collection (per Mrs. Hopkins-Jones)				1	17	6
District Collections				81	3	3
Grants:—						
From County Nursing Association	37	0	0			
From County Council Infant Life Protection	1	10	0			
From Local Education Committee, School Nursing	13	10	0			
From Welsh National Memorial Association (Tuberculosis Visiting)	5	0	0			
From County Nursing Association, Salary Grant	173	15	2			
From County Nursing Association, Mileage Grant	58	4	8			
From County Nursing Association, Telephone Grant	5	0	0			
From Castle Caereinion Charities	2	0	0			
From County Council (General Account)	22	5	0			
				318	4	10
Patients' Fees				55	5	9
Loan per Mrs. Milton Jones				75	0	0
Capital Repayment of Certificates with interest				31	10	7
Refund of Tax (due to recoding)				7	4	0
Received from Upper Banwy Association				63	3	5
Received from Nurse for use of Telephone				0	10	0
Total Receipts				643	18	4
Balance in hand at commencement of year				87	13	4
				£731	11	8

PAYMENTS.

	£	s.	d.	£	s.	d
Payments to Nurse Evans:—						
Salary (less Tax and deductions for						
Superannuation	367	12	0			
Service Grant	25	0	0			
Health Insurance and Employers' Insurance	4	7	2			
Car allowance and hire of tractor during snow	64	5	3			
Uniform and Laundry	15	0	0			
Refund of Tax (due to re-coding)	7	4	0			
				483	8	5
Telephone Charges				13	19	9
Drugs and Dressings				6	14	4
Printing and Stationery				8	4	2
Postages, cheque, stamps etc.				1	1	6
Bank charges and cheque book				1	14	6
Affiliation Fee to County Association				0	10	6
Commissioners of Inland Revenue (P.A.Y.E.)				21	13	0
A. H. Morgan (Superannuation for Nurse)				5	0	0
Hire of Committee Room				0	10	6
Due to Mrs Milton Jones on Promissory Note (Interest free loan to Llanfair Nursing Association)				75	0	0
				617	16	8
Total Payments						
Balance in the hands of the Llanfair Nursing Association				113	15	0

Certified Correct,

      O. DAVIES (Auditor),

      A. ANWYL EVANS (Hon. Treasurer).

Date: 12th June, 1947.

£731 11 8

List of Subscribers

Llanfair (in Town), District No. 1.

Collector: Mrs. A. Breeze, Arfryn.

	£	s	d
Mrs. Morris, Nantlle House	1	0	0
Mr. and Mrs. R. Cadwaladr, Midland Bank	0	10	6
Miss M. Phillips, Bridge House	0	10	6
Mr. and Mrs. Owen Davies, Brynhyfryd	0	7	6
Mrs. I. Litten, Institute Cottage	0	5	0
Rev. and Mrs. Fugh, Brynmair	0	5	0
Mrs. J. Jones, Model Bakery	0	2	6
Mr. Arthur Davies, Erfyl Terrace	0	2	0
Mr. Einion Jones, Sheffield House	0	2	6
Mr. W. W. Lewis, Manchester House	0	2	6
Mrs. W. E. Roberts, Star Shop	0	2	6
Mrs. Jones, The Institute	0	2	6
Mrs. T. Jones, Eldon House	0	2	6
Mrs. Davies, Maldwyn House	0	2	6
Mrs. D. Astley, Paris House	0	2	6
Miss Hughes, Bon Marche	0	2	6
Miss Thomas, Maenar House	0	2	6
Mr. R. Morris, Broad St. ..	0	2	6
Mr. E. Lloyd Edwards, Cambrian House	0	2	6
Mrs. D. J. Davies, Nantlle House	0	2	6

	£	s	d
Mrs. Owen, Hassall Bungalow	0	2	0
Mrs. R. Thomas, Erfyl Terrace	0	2	0
Mrs. T. Evans 3 Erfyl Terrace	0	2	0
Mrs. Stanley Evans, Hassall's Square	0	2	0
Mrs. I. O. Evans, Swan Cottage	0	2	0
Miss Jones, Fair View ..	0	2	0
Mrs. T. H. Jones, Broad St.	0	2	0
Mrs. Williams, Brook House	0	2	0
Miss S. Thomas, Institute Cottage	0	2	0
Mrs. Ralph, Rathbone Cottage	0	2	0
Mrs. Empson Davies, Bridge Street	0	2	0
Miss Jones, Old Tanhouse	0	2	0
Mr. Watkin Astley, Tanyddol	0	1	0
Mr. W. Evans, Tanyddol ..	0	1	0
Miss N. Evans. Tanyddol ..	0	1	0
Mrs. W. Roberts, Bridge St.	0	1	0
Mrs. Taylor, Institute Cottage	0	1	0
Mrs. Barker. Institute Cottage	0	1	0
	£6	3	0

Llanfair (in Town), District No. 2.

Collector: Mrs. Ingram, Police Station.

	£	s	d
Mr. and Mrs. Lewys Lloyd, Brynglas Hall	1	1	0
Mr. and Mrs. C. H. Humphreys Mount Einion ..	1	0	0
Mr. and Mrs. Hughes, N.P. Bank House	0	10	6
Mrs. Buckley and Miss Ridge, Tycrwn	0	10	0
Mr. R. Parry Jones, Bryn Banwy	0	5	0
Mr. and Miss Jehu, Brynmeurig	0	5	0

	£	s	d
Mrs. L. Goodman, Poplars	0	5	0
Mrs. Edwards, Post Office	0	5	0
Mrs. E. C. Jones Stone Villa	0	5	0
Mrs. D. W. Evans, Crown Stores	0	5	0
Miss M. Evans, Norge Villa	0	4	0
Mrs. Davies, Oaklands	0	4	0
Mrs. Williams, Dolerw-Watergate Street	0	3	6
Mrs. J. E. Hughes Hyfrydle	0	3	0

	£	s	d
Mrs. W. H. Ingram, Police Station	0	3	0
Mrs. E. Evans, Islwyn	0	3	0
Mrs. J. Williams, Goat Hotel	0	3	0
Mrs. Derrick, Commerce House	0	3	0
Mrs. Davies, Ashdale	0	2	6
Mr. and Mrs. R. Astley, Ashdale	0	2	6
Mrs. F. Twist, High St. ..	0	2	6
Mrs. E. Davies, Glasgow House	0	2	6
Mrs. Jones, Arddol	0	2	6
Mrs. T. Cork, Tymawr Cottage	0	2	6
Mrs. Chambers, Brynawel	0	2	6
Mrs. and Miss Jones, Brynbanwy	0	2	6
Mrs. Evans, Banwy View	0	2	6
Mrs. Jones, Bodeinion Villa	0	2	6
Mrs. Lloyd Pierce, Bryn Llewelyn	0	2	6
Mr. J. Lloyd Astley, Corner Shop	0	2	6
Mrs. L. Morgan, Crown House	0	2	6
Mrs. Jones, Weston House	0	2	6
Mr. Bason, Weston House	0	2	6
Mrs. D. M. Evans, Watergate Street	0	2	6
Rev. and Mrs Havard, Bodeinion	0	2	6
Mrs. J. W. Evans, Tymawr	0	2	6
Mr. D. Phillips, Watergate Street	0	2	6
Mrs. E. Pryce, Watergate Street	0	2	6
Mr. W. Pryce, Watergate St.	0	2	6
Mrs. I. Williams, Tanhouse Farm	0	2	6
Mrs. H. Tudor, Old Chapel House	0	2	6
Mrs. T. Ellis, Watergate St.	0	2	6
Mrs. M. Morris, Prescott House	0	2	6
Mrs. T. Williams, Glyn ..	0	2	6
Mrs. W. J. Watkins, Gwynfa	0	2	6
Mrs. T. E. Jones, Gernant	0	2	6
Mrs. Hughes, Wynnstay Hotel	0	2	6
Miss Jones, c/o Miss Williams, Poplars	0	2	6
Mrs. Leah, Meirionfa	0	2	0
Mrs. Morris, Bodlondeb ..	0	2	0
Mrs. Idris Williams, Bodlondeb	0	2	0
Miss Francis, Brynteg ..	0	2	0
Mrs. Norman Evans, Watergate Street	0	2	0
Mrs. Evan Morgan, Watergate Street	0	2	0
Mrs J. Breeze, Watergate Street	0	2	0
Mrs. Williams, Dolerw ..	0	2	0
Mrs. E. Morgan, Top Watergate Street	0	2	0
Mrs. Goodwin, Top Watergate Street	0	2	0
Mrs. Eaton Sunny View	0	2	0
Mrs. C. Tudor, Tanyfron	0	2	0
Mrs. Iorwerth Evans, Elkhorn	0	2	0
Mrs. T. Evans, Elkhorn ..	0	2	0
Mrs. T. H. Jones, Council Houses	0	2	0
Mrs. E. Whiffen, Council Houses	0	2	0
Mrs. J. Tudor, Wynnstay Cottage	0	2	0
Mrs. Jones, Hengefn	0	2	0
Mr. J. Williams, Goat Hotel	0	1	6
Mr. E. Jones, Llwynteg ..	0	1	0
Mrs. Jones, Armona House	0	1	0
Mr. E. Davies, Brynbanwy	0	1	0
Mrs. Lewis, Gilfach	0	1	0
Miss Williams, Poplar Cottage	0	1	0
Mrs. Jones, Bodeinion Cottage	0	1	0
Mrs. Harper, Bodeinion Cottage	0	1	0
Mrs. Bennett Aelybryn ..	0	1	0
Mr. C. Tudor, Watergate St.	0	1	0
Mrs. Bolver, High St. ..	0	1	0
Mrs. Jones, Argoed	0	1	0
Mrs. Brown, Llwyn	0	1	0
Mrs. Jones, Bronheulog ..	0	1	0
Mrs. Millington, Broncafnant	0	1	0
Mrs. Humphreys, Caethle	0	1	0
Miss Davies, Brynglas Lodge	0	1	0
Mrs. Davies, Tylissa	0	1	0
Mrs. Bolver, Poplars ..	0	0	9
Mr. J. Goodwin, Watergate Street	0	0	6
	£12	8	9

Gelligason District.

Collector: Miss C. Humphreys, Mount Einion.

	£	s	d		£	s	d
Mrs. D. Bebb, Peartree .	0	7	6	Mrs. Harris, The Mill ..	0	2	0
Mrs. Bowden, Carreg Arthur	0	3	0	Mrs. Astley, Bedwman ..	0	2	0
				Mrs. Evans, Brynawelon ..	0	2	0
Miss Richards, Gelligason	0	3	0	Mr. H. Roberts, The Bank	0	2	0
Mrs. Hudson, Red House ..	0	2	6	Mr. Bebb, The Wells	0	2	0
Mrs. Lewis Fir Bank ..	0	2	6	Mrs. Evans, Hafod Seler	0	2	0
Mrs. Jones, Dclarddyn	0	2	6	Mrs. Bumford, Rhosfawr ..	0	2	0
Mrs. Bowden, Tynybrwydd	0	2	6	Mrs. Mytton, Pantybriallen	0	2	0
Mrs. Robinson, The Firs ..	0	2	6	Mrs. Hughes, Pystyll	0	2	0
Mrs. Davies Jones, Bryntirion	0	2	6	Mrs. Blaney, Tynewydd ..	0	2	0
Mrs. Thomas, The Cwm ..	0	2	6	Mr. Davies, Lower Cilhaul	0	2	0
Mrs. Jones, The Graig	0	2	6	Mrs. Richards, Pencae ..	0	2	0
Mrs. Owen. Rhiwgoch	0	2	6	Mr. Morris, Pencoed	0	2	0
Mrs. Roberts, Yew Tree ..	0	2	6	Mr. P. Watkin, Tygwyn ..	0	1	0
Mr. Rowlands, Hydan Fawr	0	2	6	Mrs. Bowen The Ochr	0	1	0
Mrs. Morris, Mount Farm	0	2	6	Mrs. Thomas, Fronhaul ...	0	1	0
Mrs. Williams, Mount Farm	0	2	6	Mr. Bebb, Upper Cilhaul	0	1	0
Miss C. Humphreys, Mount Einion	0	2	6	Mr. Meredith, Pencoed	0	1	0
				Miss Owen, Cleniarth	0	1	0
Mrs. Bowen, Tynywern ...	0	2	6	Mrs. Isaac, Cwmgoleu	0	1	0
Mr. Bowen, Nantfforch ..	0	2	6	Mrs. Evans, Cwmgoleu....	0	1	0
Mr. J. T. Robinson, Penherber				Miss Morgan, Pencae	0	1	0
	0	2	6	A Friend	0	1	0
Mrs. Emberton Rhosfawr	0	2	0				
					£4 14	0	

Gelligason-in-Town and Brynelen District.

Collector: Mrs. A. Hewitt, Bron Einion.

	£	s	d		£	s	d
Mr. and Mrs. Maedy Jones, Preswylfa	0	10	6	Miss E. O. Davies, Bodhyfryd	0	2	6
Miss Morgan, Victoria House	0	10	0	Mrs. Powell, White Hall	0	2	6
Rev. and Mrs. Hopkins Jones, The Vicarage	0	10	0	Misses Lewis, Pantybedw ..	0	2	6
				Mrs. Chilton, The Nook ..	0	2	6
Mr. and Mrs. A. Hewitt, Bron Einion	0	5	0	Mrs. A. Breeze, Arfryn	0	2	6
				Mrs. Morgan, Brynelen ..	0	2	6
Mr. and Mrs. R. D. Hughes, Beehive	0	5	0	Mr. A. Evans, Brynelen ...	0	2	6
Mrs. Jenkins, Preswylfa	0	5	0	Mrs. Williams, Brynelen Bach	0	2	6
Mr. and Mrs. W. H. Davies, Birmingham House	0	5	0	Mrs. Thomas, Eithnog Farm	0	2	6
				Mrs. Jones, Eithnog Cottage	0	2	6
Mr. Shone Windsor House	0	4	6	Mrs. Sharpe, Eithnog Hall	0	2	6
Mrs. Morris. Lion Hotel ..	0	4	6	Mr. E. R. Shears, Bron Einion	0	2	6
Mrs. R. Lewis, Isacoed	0	4	0	Mrs. Davies, The Meadows	0	2	6
Mrs. S. Davies, Brynelen	0	4	0	Mrs. I. A. Evans, Liverpool House	0	2	6
Mrs. G. Roberts, Old Bank House	0	4	0	Mrs. O'Reilly, Bochylryd ...	0	2	0
Mrs. W. Roberts, Old Bank House	0	3	0	Mrs. J. Ll. Jones, Dolfa ...	0	2	0
				Mr. D. Lewis, Wesley St. ..	0	2	0
Mrs. E. Morgan, Talafon ..	0	2	6	Mrs. J. Evans, Newlands	0	2	0
Mrs. W. Parkes, Einion Villa	0	2	0	Mrs. E. Richards, Wesley Street	0	2	0
Mrs. Llew Jehu, Brynllys	0	2	6				

	£	s	d		£	s	d
Mrs. Evans, Brynheulog	0	2	0	Mr. Albert Thomas, Einion			
Mrs. Jones Brynpistyll	0	2	0	Cottages	0	0	6
Miss Watkin. Emporium	0	1	0				
Mrs. Rowlands, Wesley St.	0	1	0				
Mr. J. Pugh, Wesley St. ..	0	1	0				
Mrs. Williams, Einion Cottages	0	0.	6		£6	15	0

New Road and Pool Road District.
Collector: Mrs. Milton Jones, Cartref.

	£	s	d		£	s	d
Mr. T. H. Tonge, Llwyn Onn	2	0	0	Mrs. Henshaw, School House	0	2	6
Dr. and Mrs. Milton Jones, Cartref	1	1	0	Mr. E. Lewis, Station Road	0	2	6
				Mr. T. Astley, Station Road	0	2	6
Dr. and Mrs. Winstanley, Bryncoffa	0	10	0	Mrs. and Miss Williams, Vyrnwy House	0	2	6
Dr. Griffiths, Maesteg	0	7	6	Mrs. Ll. Pierce, Llwynderw	0	2	0
Mr. and Mrs. Jones, Caerberllan	0	6	0	Mrs. Whiffen, Pool Road ..	0	2	0
				Miss L. Williams Pool Road	0	2	0
Mrs. and Miss Jones, Maesteg	0	5	0	Mr. T. James, Pool Road ..	0	2	0
				Mr. J. Lewis, Pool Road ...	0	2	0
Mr. and Mrs. J. Ll. Peate, Glan Einion	0	5	0	Mr. Leah, Pool Road	0	2	0
				Miss Jones, Pool Road ..	0	2	0
Mr. S. Evans, Bryndedwyth	0	5	0	Mrs. R. Goodwin, Pool Road	0	1	6
				Mrs. Emberton, Poo Road ..	0	1	6
Miss F. Haynes, Cartref ..	0	5	0	Mrs. Emberton, Pool Road	0	1	6
Misses Williams Brynavon	0	5	0	Miss E. Astley, The Garage	0	1	0
Mr. J. Richards. Vyrnwy Villa	0	4	0	Mrs. Clifford Leah, Pool Road	0	1	0
Mrs. Tonge, Brynavon	0	3	0	Miss Owen, Pool Road	0	1	0
Mrs. E. Astley, Park View	0	2	6	Mrs. Vic Jones, Pool Road	0	1	0
Mrs. D. Peate, The Mill	0	2	6				
Mrs. Bert Peate, The Mill	0	2	6		£7	18	6
Mrs. Hughes. Ivy Cottage	0	2	6				

Rhosaflo District.
Collector: Mrs. Madryn Jones, Llys Myfyr.

	£	s	d		£	s	d
Rev. and Mrs. Madryn Jones, Llys Myfyr	0	6	0	Mrs. Rees, Rhosaflo	0	2	6
Mrs. Thomas, Smithy	0	5	0	Mr. T. M. Evans, Caellewelyn	0	2	6
Mrs. Edwards, Neuadd ..	0	5	0	Mrs. Owen Allt Isaf (1945—46)	0	2	6
Mrs. Williams Penwtra ..	0	5	0				
Miss Griffiths, Bethlehem	0	4	0	Mr. Thomas. Cwmllwynog	0	2	0
Mrs. Edwards, Wern	0	3	6	M. Trow, Co.dygarth!wyd	0	2	0
Mrs. Astley, Glanbanw ..	0	3	6	Mrs. Isaac, Caellewelyn....	0	2	0
Misses Rees, Tynllwyn	0	3	0	Mrs. Omri Jones, Banw House	0	2	0
Mrs. Stephens, Maesyglydfa	0	2	6	Mrs. Williams, Pentalcefn	0	2	0
Mrs. O. Jones, Allt Ucha	0	2	0	Mr. I. R. Roberts, Smithy...	0	2	0
Mrs. Watkins. Pantgwyn ..	0	2	6	Mrs. Evans, Brynrefail ..	0	1	0
Mrs. Owen. Allt Isaf ..	0	2	6				
Mrs. Watkins, Bronygarth	0	2	0		£3	13	6
Mrs. Evans, Stingwern ..	0	2	0				
Mrs. Hudson, Tynyfron ..	0	2	6				

Heniarth District.

Collector: Mrs. T. Watkin, Heniarth Mill.

	£	s	d		£	s	d
Capt. and Mrs. Griffiths, Brynfa ....:...	1	1	0	Mrs. Davies, Heniarth Farm	0	2	6
Mr. and Mrs. Dean Jones, Glanafon	0	5	0	Mrs. J. T. Watkins Heniarth Mill	0	2	6
Mrs. Hughes, Heniarth Gate	0	3	6	Mrs. G. Davies, Heniarth Mill	0	2	6
Mrs. Bowen, Dolrhyd ..	0	2	6	Mrs. Pierce, Tanilan Cottage	0	1	0
Mrs. J. W. Jones, Tany-bryn	0	2	6				
Mrs Price, Tanllan Farm	0	2	6		£2	5	6

Llangyniew District No. 1.

Collector: Mrs. Haynes, Caethle.

	£	s	d		£	s	d
Mr. and Mrs. R. T. Wood, Heulfron	0	10	6	Mrs. Emberton	0	2	6
Mrs. F. S. Gwilt	0	10	0	Mrs. Edwards, Tan-yr-hafcd	0	2	6
Mrs. Robinson, Cefndu	0	5	0	Mrs. Roberts, Henllan Mill	0	2	6
Mrs. Emberton, Oakfields	0	5	0	Mrs. Lewis, Henllan Mill	0	2	6
Mrs. Pugh, Glascoed Bach	0	5	0	Miss E. Jones, Noddfa	0	2	6
Mrs. Haynes, Caethle	0	2	6	Miss E. Jones, Aelybryn ..	0	2	6
Miss Owen, Caethle	0	2	6	Mrs. Bebb, Hafodlwyd ..	0	2	0
Mrs. S. Swain, Gas Cottage	0	2	6	Mrs. Davies, Tybrith	0	2	0
Mrs. E. A. Lewis, Tyncoed	0	2	6	Mrs. Thomas Smithy ..	0	2	0
Mrs. Evans, Brwyn	0	2	6	Mrs. E. Watkins, Maesy-groes	0	2	0
Mrs. Williams, Tynywern	0	2	6	Mrs. Jones, Glascoed	0	2	0
Mrs. Roberts, Hafodlwyd ..	0	2	6	Mrs. Davies, Hyden Cottage	0	2	0
Mrs. Foulkes, Penybont ..	0	2	6	Mrs. Lewis, Tyncoed	0	2	0
Mrs. Owen, The Lodge	0	2	6	Mrs. Meredith, Glascoed	0	1	6
Mr. J. B. Thomas, The Lodge	0	2	6	Mrs. Jones, Caethle	0	1	6
Mrs. Jones, Chapel House	0	2	6	Mrs. E. Jones	0	1	0
Mrs. Jones, Glascoed Villa	0	2	6				
Mrs. R. Swain, Gas Cottage	0	2	6				
Mrs. Morgan, Gas Cottage	0	2	0		£5	0	0

Llangyniew District No. 2.

Collector: Mrs. D. J. Williams, Delfan.

	£	s	d		£	s	d
Rev. and Mrs. James, Llangyniew Rectory	0	10	0	Mrs. Smith School House	0	2	6
Mrs. Sherwen, Henllan Fach	0	3	0	Mrs. Williams, Delfan	0	2	6
Mrs. Williams, Tymawr ..	0	2	6	Mrs. Jones, Tyddyn	0	2	6
Miss Jarman, Henllan ..	0	2	6	Mrs. Williams, Minffordd	0	2	6
Mrs. Jarman, Henllan ..	0	2	6	Miss Lllidye, Mount Pleasant	0	2	6
Mrs. Davies, Cefnllwyd ..	0	2	6	Miss Morris, Henllan	0	2	0
Mrs. Watkin, Cefnllwyd ..	0	2	6				
Mrs. Jones, Pentre	0	2	6				
Mrs. Jones, Pen Pentre	0	2	6		£2	4	6

Llanoddian District No. 2.

Collector: Mrs J. W. Jones, Tanybryn.

Mr. and Mrs. Stanley Hughes, Garthlwyd	0 5 0	Mrs. R. Jones, Pentre	0 2 6
Mrs. Griffiths, Garthlwyd	0 5 0	Mrs. Jones, Gwynyndy ..	0 2 6
Mrs. Davies, Pentrebach	0 3 0	Mrs. Richards, Llanoddian	0 2 6
Mrs. Haynes, Llanoddian	0 2 6		
Miss Jones, Neuadd	0 2 6	£1 5 6

Pencaedu District.

Collector: Mrs. E. Williams, Neuaddcynhinfa.

Mr. and Mrs. Lomas, Tanhouse Hotel	0 10 0	Mr. and Mrs. Williams, Tanhouse Farm	0 2 6
Mr. and Miss Lloyd Rhosymenyn	0 5 0	Mr. and Miss Thomas, Graigwen	0 2 6
Mrs. Griffiths, Cynhinia ..	0 5 0	Mr. and Mrs. Lloyd, Pantanhouse	0 2 6
Mr. and Mrs. Harding, Neuadd	0 5 0	Mr. Williams, Llanoddian	0 2 6
Mr. and Mrs. Hughes, Pencaedu	0 4 6	Mr. and Mrs. Roberts Pennal Chapel House	0 2 6
Mr. and Mrs. Davies, Maesneuadd	0 4 6	Mr. and Mrs. Griffiths, Tyrnpic	0 2 6
Mr. and Mrs. Watkins, Pantanhouse	0 3 0	Mr. Stephens, Graigwen ..	0 2 6
Mr. and Mrs. Williams, Neuadd	0 2 6	Mr. and Mrs. Thomas, Penyffordd	0 2 6
Mrs. Jones, Plascoch	0 2 6	Mr. and Mrs. Jones, Groesddu	0 2 0
Mr. Griffiths, Plascoch	0 2 6	Mrs. Hughes, Topia	0 2 0
Mr. and Mrs. Edwards, Henefail	0 2 6	Mr. E. Lloyd, Topia	0 2 0
Mr. and Mrs. Thomas, Efailweeg	0 2 0	Miss Jones, Pantanhouse	0 2 0
Mr. and Mrs. Jones, Broncynhinfa	0 2 0	Mr. G. Edwards, Henefail ..	0 1 6
Mr. and Mrs. Richards, Tygwyn	0 2 6	Mrs. Thomas, Efailweeg	0 1 0
		£4 5 0	

Pentyrch District.

Collectors: Misses M. and L. Roberts, Tynyberth.

Mrs. Jones, Cefndre	0 3 0	Mrs. Roberts, Henefail	0 2 6
Mrs. Bebb, Hendre	0 3 0	Mrs. Griffiths, Troedyrewig	0 2 6
Mr. R. Davies, Hirros Ucha	0 2 6	Miss Corbett, Cefngoleu ..	0 2 6
Mrs. J. Roberts, Tynyberth	0 2 6	Mrs. Jones, Pentyrch Farm	0 2 6
Mrs. Jones, Gors	0 2 6	Mrs. Owens, Coedcaehaidd	0 2 0
Mrs. Owens, Four Crosses	0 2 6	Mr. Davies, Erw	0 2 0
Mrs. Meredith Tynewydd	0 2 6	Mr. Llowarch, Coedcaehaidd	0 1 0
Mrs. Davies. Gyfylchau ..	0 2 6		
Mrs. Jones, Tynygerddu	0 2 6	£2 3 6	
Mrs. Jones, Gelli	0 2 6		
Mrs. Jones, Gelli Cottage	0 2 6		

'Rhiwhiriaeth' District.

Collector: Mrs. Tudor, Pantgelynen.

Mrs. Jones, Rhiwhiriaeth	0	2	6	Mr. James Astley, Melinddol	0	2	6
Mrs. Haynes, Rhiwhiriaeth	0	2	6	Mrs. Davies, Tymawr	0	2	6
Mrs. Lewis, Dolgelynen ..	0	2	6	Miss N. Craig, Brook House	0	2	6
Mrs. Wilson Glynhiriaeth ..	0	2	6	Mrs. Evans, Parkyrhiew..	0	2	6
Mrs. Watkins, Brynhiriaeth	0	2	6	Mr. J. Watkin, Parkyrhiew	0	2	0
Miss Llywarch and Mr. E.				Mrs. Watkin, Froneithin ..	0	2	0
Morgan, Rhiwhiriaeth ..	0	2	6	Mrs. Jones, The Mill	0	2	0
Mrs. Evans, Tyucha	0	2	6	Miss Dilys Roberts, Tynpant	0	2	0
Mrs. Hughes, Wernhir ..	0	2	6	Mrs. Jones, Shop	0	1	0
Mrs. Tudor, Pantgelynen	0	2	6	Mrs. Davies, Melinddol	0	1	0
Mrs. Williams, Cilhaul	0	2	6	Mrs. Morgan, Melinddol ..	0	1	0
Mrs. Roberts, Tynpant ..	0	2	6	Mrs. Roberts, Melinddol ..	0	1	0
Mrs. Davies, Pantygroes ..	0	2	6	Mr. Arwyn Roberts, Melin-			
Mrs. Astley, Melinddol ...	0	2	6	ddol	0	1	0
Mrs. Davies and Miss Jones,							
Melinddol	0	2	6		£2	17	6

Brynglas and Dolgead District No. 1.

Collector: Miss Savage, Caenymynydd.

Miss Evans, Broneilin ..	0	10	0	Mrs. Evans, Tynrhos Uchaf	0	2	0
Mrs. Hughes, Dolgead Hall	0	5	0	Mrs. Oliver, Rhydarwydd	0	2	0
Mr. W. Vaughan Williams,				Mrs. Williams, Bronffynon	0	2	0
Pengraig	0	5	0	Mrs. Ellis, Berthfawr	0	2	0
Mrs. James, Gro	0	3	0	Mrs. Evans, Brynglas	0	2	0
Mrs. Morris, Brynglocsin	0	3	0	Mrs. Jones Fronhaul	0	2	0
Mrs. Evans, Dolgead	0	2	0	Mrs. Edwards, Brynglas			
Mrs. Roberts, Brynglas Hall	0	2	6	Bach	0	2	0
Mrs. Evans, Pencoming ...	0	2	6	Mr. Hugh Ellis, Berthfawr	0	2	0
Mrs. Jones, Penybryn ..	0	2	6	Mrs. Jones, Tynrhos Isaf ..	0	2	0
Mrs. T. Edwards, Brynglas				Mrs. Williams, Tyddyn	0	2	0
Bach	0	2	6	Mrs. Davies, Cae-eithin ..	0	1	0
Mrs. Owen, Pencreigiau ..	0	2	6				
Mrs. Savage, Caenymynydd	0	2	6		£3	6	6
Miss N. Evans, Broneilin ..	0	2	0				

Brynglas and Dolgead District No. 2.

Collector: Miss Humphreys, Tirdu.

Miss Griffiths, Gartheilin ..	0	2	6	Mrs. Williams, Brynhyfryd	0	2	0
Mrs. Edwards, Hendy	0	2	6	Miss Rees, Tynywig	0	2	0
Mrs. Davies, Wernywig ..	0	2	6	Miss Owens, Weeg Fach ..	0	2	0
Mrs. Lewis, Moeldrahaiarn	0	2	6	Mrs. Roberts, Tymawr	0	1	0
Mrs. Humphreys, Tirdu ..	0	2	6	Mrs. Evans, Weeg			
Mrs. Evans, Buarthbachog	0	2	0				
Mrs. Jones, Gwaenynog ..	0	2	0		£1	6	6
Miss M. Blainey, Glanllyn	0	2	0				

· Penarth District.

Collectors: Mrs Huxley, Pentre, and Mrs. Thomas, Tygwyn.

Mrs. Thomas, Tygwyn	0	5	0	Mrs. Thomas, Cwmllwyn-			
Mrs. Davies, Llwyngwyn ..	0	2	6	gwyn	0	2	0
Mrs. Jones, Penlan	0	2	6	Mrs. Buckley, Pant	0	2	0
Mrs. Huxley, Pentre	0	2	6	Mrs. Owen, Penrhiew	0	2	0
Mrs. Roberts, Tycapel	0	2	6	Mrs. Davies, Adwywynt ..	0	2	0
Mrs. Jones, Frongoch	0	2	6	Mrs. Evans, Mill	0	2	0
Mrs. Lloyd, Fron	0	2	6	Mrs. Evans, Ffrydiau	0	2	0
Mrs. Jones, White Lane ..	0	2	6	Mrs. Tudor, Coed	0	1	0
Mrs. Buckley, Tyncelyn ..	0	2	6	Mrs. Watkins, Bronfedw	0	1	0
Mrs. Watkins, Penarth ..	0	2	6	Mrs. Phillips, Glog	0	1	0
Mrs. Roberts, Plasiolyn ..	0	2	6	Mrs. Phillips, Brynpenarth	0	1	0
Mrs. Thomas, Mount Plea-				Mrs. Benting, Caerwedyn	0	1	0
sant	0	2	6				
Mrs. Owen, Hafod-y-Gan ..	0	2	6		£2	14	0
Mrs. Jepson, Gaer	0	2	0				

Llanfair Upper District.

Collector: Miss M. E. Hughes, Rhiwhiriaeth, School House.

Mrs. Jones, Nantcae	0	3	0	Mrs. Jones, Tynyfownog ..	0	2	0
Mrs. Humphreys, Pencwm	0	3	0	Mr. Roberts, Rhosgoch ..	0	2	0
Mrs. Williams, Glyndwr	0	3	0	Mrs. Tanner, Ystrad	0	1	0
Mrs. Jones, Pengelli	0	2	6	Mrs. Watkins, Bryngwewyr	0	1	0
Mrs. Pugh, Cefn Parc ..	0	2	6	Mrs. Hughes, Pencraig	0	1	0
Miss M. E. Hughes, School				Mrs. Thomas, Llefy	0	1	0
House ....,...	0	2	6	Mrs. Jones, Tynywerglodd	0	1	0
Mrs. Morgan, Ystrad	0	2	6	Miss Watkins, Dolau	0	1	0
Mr. E. R. Jones, Cross ..	0	2	6	Mrs. Evans, Rhiwhiriaeth			
Mrs. Jones, Wenallt	0	2	0	Uchaf	0	1	0
Mrs. Savage, Tangraig	0	2	0	Mrs. Bennett, Cross	0	1	0
Mrs. Bennett, Siloh Chapel				Mrs. Evans, Tyisa	0	1	0
House	0	2	0	Mr. Watkins, Glyn Ucha	0	1	0
Mrs. Evans, Pantglas	0	2	0	Mrs. Astley, Tynglyn	0	1	0
Mrs. Jones, Bryn Tawel ..	0	2	0	Mrs. Williams, Waenbitfel	0	1	0
Mrs. Hughes, Groesfer	0	2	0		£2	11	0
Mrs. Astley, Gwernybrain	0	2	0				

Cefncoch District No. 1.

Collectors: Mrs. Jones, Frongoch Hall, and Mrs. Andrew, Bryngwyn.

Mr. and Mrs. Jones, Fron-				Mr. and Mrs. Watkins, Min-			
goch Hall	0	5	0	ffordd	0	3	6
Miss Threadgold, Cefncoch				Mr. and Mrs. Richards, Car-			
Hotel	0	5	0	regybig	0	2	6
Mrs. D. E. Jones, Gorsdyf-				Miss Jones, Drain	0	2	6
wch	0	5	0	Mrs. Watkins, Gwaenydd ..	0	2	6
Mrs. Jones, Tynewydd ..	0	5	0	Mrs. Watkins, Nantwyllt	0	2	6
Mr. and Mrs. Morris, Haf-				Mrs. Watkins, Dolyfardyn-			
odsych	0	3	6	fawr	0	2	6

Mrs. Morris, Cwm	0	2	(	Mrs. Benbow, Cefnbryn	0	2	0
Mrs. Andrew, Bryngwyn	0	2	(	Mrs. Haynes, Tycerrig	0	2	0
Mrs. Jones, Bendy Hir	0	2	6	Mrs. Evans, Waenymaglau	0	2	0
Miss Hughes, Bendy Hir	0	2	6				
Mrs. Thomas, Tyncoed	0	2	(	Mrs. Thomas, Penrhosydd	0	2	0
Mrs. Griffiths Fronhaul	0	2	(				
Mrs. Jones, Highfield	0	2	:				
Mrs. Andrew, Bleak House	0	2	(		£3	10	0
Mrs. Huxley, Smithy	0	2	(				

Cefncoch District No. 2.

Collector: Miss Megan Watkin, Tybrith.

Mrs. Buckley, Tymawr	0	3	0	Mrs. Williams Lawnt	0	2	6
Mrs. Lewis, Erwhen	0	3	0	Mrs. Jones, Bronffynon	0	2	6
Mrs. Watkin, Pendwyrhiew	0	3	0	Mrs. Ashton, Lawnt Uchaf	0	2	0
Mrs. Evans, Tybrith	0	3	(	Mrs. Evans, School House	0	0	6
Mrs. Davies, Llwynrhyddod	0	2	(				
Mr. Williams, Pendwyrhiew	0	2	(		£1	7	0
Mrs. Watkin, Tybrith	0	2	(				

Cefncoch District No. 3.

Collector: Miss Mona Williams, Belanddu.

Miss Williams, Hendai	0	5	0	Mrs. Bennett, Caebryn	0	2	0
Mrs. Ashton, Belanddu	0	5	0	Miss Hughes, Sychnant	0	2	0
Mr. J. Watkin, Upper Mill	0	5	0	Mrs. Williams, Bryngrugog	0	2	0
Mrs. W. Morris, Vicarage	0	5	0	Mrs. Jones, Sylfaen	0	2	0
Mrs. J. P. Humphreys, Ddol	0	4	0	Mrs. Jones, Tybach	0	2	0
Mr. Morgan, Frongreen	0	3	6	Mrs. Huxley, Rhosyddgwyn-			
Mrs. D. Lewis, Pencoed	0	3	0	ion	0	2	0
Mrs. Williams, Ebrandy	0	3	0	Mrs. Davies, Tynllan	0	2	0
Mrs. E. Turner, Penddol	0	2	6	Mrs. Hughes, Stone Cottage	0	2	0
Mrs. Watkin Glanyrafon	0	2	6	Mrs. Williams New House	0	2	0
Mrs. Thomas, Buerthgerrig	0	2	6	Mrs. Watkin, Fuchesgoch	0	2	0
Miss Richards, Gwernfyda	0	2	6	Miss Lewis, Rhydbiswel	0	2	0
Mr. Jones, Plashelig	0	2	6				
Mrs. Humphreys, Tyhir	0	2	6				
Mrs. Evans, Belan	0	2	6		£3	15	0
Mrs. Davies, Fron	0	2	0				

Horeb District

Collector: Miss Glenys Roberts, Dolfardyn Fach.

Mrs. Roberts, Dolyfardyn Fach	0	2	6	Mrs. Oliver, Lluast Mathew	0	1	0
Mrs. Jones, Llettygwilym	0	2	6	Mrs. Humphreys, Penywaen	0	1	0
Mrs. Wi liams, Llettygiwlym Uchaf	0	2	6	Mrs. Jones, Pantywaen	0	1	0
				Mrs. Davies, Pantymilwyr	0	1	0
Mrs. Williams, Penffridd	0	2	0	Mr. Jones, Llettymilwyr	0	1	0
Mrs. Evans, Bronffynon	0	2	0				
Mrs. Morgan, Foel	0	2	0		£0	18	6

County Times, Printers, Welshpool.

Select Bibliography

Doylerush, E. (1993) *Fallen Eagles. A Guide to Aircraft Crashes in North-east and Mid Wales*, Midland Counties Publications, Leicester.

Drake Software Associates (2001) *Value of the Pound, 1600-1999*, version 3. Available from Drake Software, 1 Wychwood Rise, Great Missendum, Bucks, HP16 0HB.

Gwilym, Ifor ap (1978) *Hanes y Traddodiad Cerddorol yng Nghymru*, Abertawe: Christopher Davies.

Pryce, W.T.R. (1991) *The Photographer in Rural Wales. A Photographic Archive of Llanfair Caereinion and its Region, c.1865-1986*. Llanfair Caereinion: The Powysland Club.

Strange, A. (1983) *Me Dad's the Village Blacksmith*. Denbigh: Gee and Son Ltd.

Strange, A. (1986) *Following Me Dad*. Denbigh: Gee and Son Ltd.

Index – *the bold type refers to pages with figures.*

165

166